Higher
Chemistry
Practice Papers for SQA Exams

Barry McBride

Contents

The instructions and answer grid for completion of Section 1 in each practice paper can be downloaded from www.hoddereducation.co.uk/updatesandextras

The Publishers would like to thank the following for permission to reproduce copyright material:

Photo credits p.47 © GP Library Limited/Alamy Stock Photo; **p.67** © Pictorial Press Ltd/Alamy Stock Photo.

Acknowledgements Exam rubrics at the start of each paper copyright © Scottish Qualifications Authority; Diagram on p.79 and p.118 copyright © Scottish Qualifications Authority.

Every effort has been made to trace all copyright holders, but if any have been inadvertently overlooked the Publishers will be pleased to make the necessary arrangements at the first opportunity.

Although every effort has been made to ensure that website addresses are correct at time of going to press, Hodder Gibson cannot be held responsible for the content of any website mentioned in this book. It is sometimes possible to find a relocated web page by typing in the address of the home page for a website in the URL window of your browser.

Hachette UK's policy is to use papers that are natural, renewable and recyclable products and made from wood grown in sustainable forests. The logging and manufacturing processes are expected to conform to the environmental regulations of the country of origin.

Orders: please contact Bookpoint Ltd, 130 Park Drive, Milton Park, Abingdon, Oxon OX14 4SE. Telephone: (44) 01235 827720. Fax: (44) 01235 400454. Lines are open 9.00–5.00, Monday to Saturday, with a 24-hour message answering service. Visit our website at www.hoddereducation.co.uk. Hodder Gibson can be contacted direct on: Tel: 0141 333 4650; Fax: 0141 404 8188; email: hoddergibson@hodder.co.uk

First published in 2017 by
Hodder Gibson, an imprint of Hodder Education,
An Hachette UK Company
211 St Vincent Street
Glasgow G2 5Q4

Impression number   5 4 3 2 1
Year   2021 2020 2019 2018 2017

Cover photo © ssilver/123RF.com
Illustrations by Aptara, Inc.
Typeset in Din regular 12/14.4 by Aptara, Inc.
Printed in the UK.

A catalogue record for this title is available from the British Library.

ISBN: 978 1 5104 1352 8

Introduction

Higher Chemistry

The course

Before sitting your Higher Chemistry examination you must have passed three Unit Assessments within your school or college.

To achieve a pass in Higher Chemistry there are then two further components.

Component 1 – The assignment

You are required to submit an assignment that is worth 17% (20 marks) of your final grade. This assignment will be based on research and may include an experiment. This assignment requires you to apply skills, knowledge and understanding to investigate a relevant topic in chemistry and its effect on the environment and/or society. Your school or college will provide you with a candidate's guide for this assignment, which has been produced by the SQA. This guide gives guidance on what is required to complete the report and gain as many marks as possible.

Your assignment report will be marked by the SQA.

Component 2 – The question paper

The question paper will assess breadth and depth of knowledge and understanding from across all of the three units.

The question paper will require you to:

- demonstrate your knowledge and understanding of chemistry by making statements, describing information, providing explanations and integrating knowledge
- apply your chemistry knowledge to new situations, analysing information and solving problems
- plan and design experiments/practical investigations to test given hypotheses or to illustrate particular effects including safety measures
- select information and present information appropriately in a variety of forms
- process information (using calculations and units, where appropriate)
- make predictions and generalisations from evidence/information
- draw valid conclusions and give explanations supported by evidence
- evaluate experiments/practical investigations and suggest improvements.

To achieve a 'C' grade in Higher Chemistry you must achieve at least 50% of the 120 marks available when the two components, i.e. the question paper and the assignment, are combined. For a 'B' grade you will need 60%, while for an 'A' grade you must ensure that you gain as many of the marks available as possible and at least 70%.

This book contains practice papers that cover the content of the Higher Chemistry course and illustrate the standard, structure and requirements of the question paper that you will sit during the exam.

Each practice paper consists of two sections. (A detailed marking scheme for each section is provided at the end of this book.)

- Section A will contain objective questions (multiple choice) and will have 20 marks.
- Section B will contain restricted and extended response questions and will have 80 marks.

Each practice paper contains a variety of questions, including those that require:

- demonstration and application of knowledge and understanding of the mandatory content of the course from across the three units
- application of scientific inquiry skills.

How to use this book

This book can be used in three ways:

1. You can complete an entire practice paper under exam conditions, without the use of books or notes. Then mark the papers using the marking scheme provided. This method gives you a clear indication of the level you are working at and should highlight the content areas that you need to work on before attempting the next practice paper. This method allows you to see your progress as you complete each practice paper.

2. You can complete a practice paper using your notes and books. Try the question first and then refer to your notes if you are unable to answer the question. The detailed marking scheme also provides information to help you understand the answers given. This is a form of studying and by doing this you will be covering all the areas of content that you are weakest in. You should notice that you are referring to your notes less with each practice paper completed.

3. The revision grid allows you to target a specific area of the course. If for example you feel that you need to concentrate more on periodicity, then the revision grid lists all the questions based on periodicity across the three papers.

Try to practise as many questions as possible. This will get you used to the language used in the question papers and ultimately improve your chances of success.

Hints and tips

Below is a list of hints and tips that will help you to achieve your full potential in the Higher Chemistry exam:

- Ensure that you **read each question carefully**. Scanning the question and missing the main points results in mistakes being made. Some students highlight the main points of a question with a highlighter pen to ensure that they don't miss anything out.
- Open-ended questions include the statement '**Using your knowledge of chemistry**'. These questions provide you with an opportunity to 'show off' your chemistry knowledge. To obtain the 3 marks on offer for these questions you must demonstrate a good understanding of the chemistry involved and provide a logically correct answer to the question posed. Open questions have no one correct answer. Listed in the marking scheme are **some** of the options that may be included and explained in your answer. This list is not exhaustive and you do not have to include all of these to gain the full 3 marks.

Ensure that what you have included has been explained fully and clearly. Include diagrams, equations etc. that may help with your explanation.

- When doing calculations ensure that you **show all your working**. If you make a simple arithmetical mistake you may still be awarded some of the marks but only if your working is laid out clearly so that the examiner can see where you went wrong and what you did correctly. Just giving the answers is very risky and you should always show your working.
- **Attempt all questions**. Leaving questions blank means that you will definitely not gain the mark.
- If you are asked to explain in a question, then you must **explain your answer fully**. For example, if you are asked to explain fully the change in covalent radius going down a group in the periodic table then you cannot simply say:

'It increases going down a group.'

This answer tells the examiner the trend but to gain the marks you must explain the trend fully:

'Covalent radius increases going down a group because atoms have more energy levels going down a group. This means that the outer electrons are further from the nucleus and the shielding by the inner energy levels means that the nucleus has less influence on the outer electrons.'

Including diagrams or equations in your answers to 'explain fully' and open questions can greatly help with your explanation. For example:

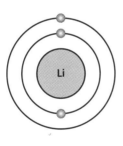 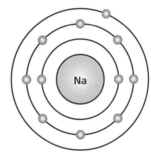

Lithium 2,1   Sodium 2,8,1

- **Use your data booklet** when you are asked to write formulas, ionic formulas, formula mass, etc. The data booklet is there so use it to double check the numbers you require.
- Work on your **timing**. The multiple-choice section (Section 1) should take approximately 30–45 minutes. Attempt to answer the multiple-choice questions before you look at the four possible answers, as this will improve your confidence. Use scrap paper when required to scribble down structural formulas, calculations, chemical formulas, etc. as this will reduce your chance of making errors. If you are finding the question difficult, try to eliminate the obviously wrong answers to increase your chances.
- When asked to **predict** or **estimate** based on information from a graph or a table, take your time to look for patterns. For example, if asked to predict a boiling point, try to establish if there is a regular change in boiling point and use that regular pattern to establish the unknown boiling point.
- When drawing a **diagram** of an experiment ask yourself the question, 'Would this work if I set it up exactly like this in the lab?' Ensure that the method you have drawn would produce the desired results *safely*. If, for example, you are heating a flammable reactant such as alcohol

then you will not gain the marks if you heat it with a Bunsen burner in your diagram; a water bath would be much safer! Make sure your diagram is labelled clearly.

Remember that the rewards for passing Higher Chemistry are well worth it! Your pass will help you get the future you want for yourself. In the exam, be confident in your own ability. If you are not sure how to answer a question, trust your instincts and just give it a go anyway. Keep calm and don't panic.

Good luck!

Revision grid

SQA Unit	Paper A		Paper B		Paper C	
	Section 1 questions	Section 2 questions	Section 1 questions	Section 2 questions	Section 1 questions	Section 2 questions
Unit 1 – Chemical Changes and Structure						
Controlling the rate	4, 8	6c)(ii)	3, 6	10c)(iii), 11d)(ii)	3	4a)
Periodicity	1	5a), 5b), 5c), 5d)	4, 5	8a), 8c), 8d), 8e)(i), 8e)(ii)	1, 2, 5	11a), 11b)(i), 11b)(iii)
Structure and bonding	3	1a), 12c)	1, 2	2a), 2b), 3a)	4	1a), 2a), 6d)(ii), 10b)
Unit 2 – Nature's Chemistry						
Esters, fats and oils	6, 7, 9, 15	9a)(i), 9a)(ii), 9b)(ii), 9d)		5a), 5b)(i), 5b)(ii)	7, 8	6a), 6b), 6c), 14a), 14b)(i), 14b)(ii), 14b)(iii)
Proteins	12	12a)(i), 12a)(ii)	10	11a), 11b)(i), 11b)(ii)	10	2b), 2c)
Chemistry of cooking		12b)	7, 8	12a), 11c)		7a)
Oxidation of food	11	1b)(i), 7a)(ii), 11b), 11c)	11	12b), 12c)	9,11	2b), 7b), 8b)(ii)
Soaps, detergents and emulsions	10		9, 12	5c), 9a), 9b), 9c)		8a)(i), 8a)(ii)
Fragrances		4a), 4c)(i), 4c)(ii)			6	8b)(i), 8c)
Skin care		6b)(i), 6b)(ii)				12a)(i), 12a)(ii), 12b), 12c), 12d)(i), 12d)(ii)
Unit 3 – Chemistry in Society						
Getting the most from reactants	17	4b), 4d)(ii), 6a)(iii), 6c)(i), 9b)(i)	14, 15	3b)(i), 5d)(iii), 10b), 10c)(ii)	15	1c), 1e)(iii), 4b)(ii), 10c), 10d)
Equilibrium	16	10a), 10b), 10c), 10d), 10e)		3c)	12, 14	5a), 5c), 14b)(iv)
Chemical energy		3a), 3b), 12e)	13, 18	1b), 7a)(ii), 7b)(iii)	16, 17	7c)
Oxidising or reducing agents	14, 18, 19	6a)(i)	17, 19	1c)(i), 1c)(ii), 7c)(i), 10c)(i)	13, 18, 19	1b)

SQA Unit	Paper A		Paper B		Paper C	
	Section 1 questions	**Section 2 questions**	**Section 1 questions**	**Section 2 questions**	**Section 1 questions**	**Section 2 questions**
Chemical analysis	5, 20	3c), 7c)(i), 7c)(ii), 7c)(iii), 11a)(i), 11a)(ii)	16, 20	3b)(iii), 7a)(iii), 11d)(i)	20	1e)(i), 1e)(ii), 4b)(i), 6d)(i)
Open questions	2 and 8		4 and 6		3 and 9	
Problem solving	2, 13	1b)(ii), 4d)(i), 6a)(ii), 7a)(i), 7b), 9c), 11d), 12d)		1a)(i), 1a)(ii), 3b)(ii), 5d)(i), 5d)(ii), 7a)(i), 7b)(i), 7b)(ii), 7c)(ii), 8b), 10a)		1d), 1f), 5b), 10a), 11b)(ii), 12c)(ii), 13a), 13b)(i), 13b)(ii), 13c)(i),

Higher
Chemistry

A

Reference may be made to the Chemistry Higher and Advanced Higher Data Booklet.

Duration – 2 hours and 30 minutes

Total marks – 100

SECTION 1 – 20 marks

Attempt ALL questions.

SECTION 2 – 80 marks

Attempt ALL questions

Write your answers clearly in the spaces provided in this paper. Additional space for answers and rough work is provided at the end of this paper. If you use this space you must clearly identify the question number you are attempting. Any rough work must be written in this space. You should score through your rough work when you have written your final copy.

Use **blue** or **black** ink.

Section 1

Total marks: 20

Attempt **ALL** questions. Answer grid available at www.hoddereducation.co.uk/updatesandextras.

1 Which of the following compounds has the greatest ionic character?

   A Sodium fluoride
   B Sodium chloride
   C Sodium bromide
   D Sodium iodide

2 Particles with the same electron arrangement are said to be isoelectronic.
   Which of the following compounds contains ions that are isoelectronic?

   A LiF
   B Na_2O
   C $CaBr_2$
   D $AlCl_3$

3 Which of the following is an example of a van der Waals force?

   A Metallic bond
   B Covalent bond
   C Hydrogen bond
   D Polar covalent bond

4 The diagram below shows the energy profile for a reaction.

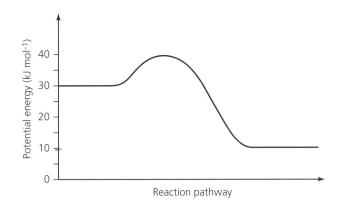

What is the enthalpy change, in $kJ\,mol^{-1}$, for the **reverse** reaction?

   A −20
   B +20
   C −30
   D +30

5 The average kinetic energy of the particles in a substance can be measured using a

   A standard flask

   B thermometer

   C balance

   D pipette.

6 The following compound is found in the scent of carnations.

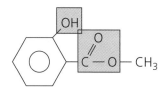

Which functional groups are highlighted in this compound?

   A Carbonyl and hydroxyl

   B Ester link and carboxyl

   C Carbonyl and carboxyl

   D Ester link and hydroxyl

7 Which of the following reactions converts vegetable oils into vegetable fats?

   A Dehydrogenation

   B Hydrogenation

   C Condensation

   D Hydrolysis

8 The graph shows how the rate of a chemical reaction varies with temperature.

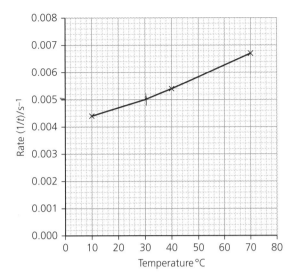

Calculate the reaction time, in seconds, when the temperature of the reaction mixture was 30°C.

A 0.005

B 0.15

C 20

D 200

9 Which of the following can be classed as an ester?

A Fat

B Soap

C Glycerol

D Fatty acid

10 Emulsifiers are commonly added to food to

A prevent oxidation

B reduce the calorific value

C reduce the saturated fat content

D prevent oil and water soluble molecules separating into layers.

11 Which of the following molecules would **not** react with acidified potassium dichromate?

A
$$
\begin{array}{c}
\quad\ \ H\quad CH_3\ H \\
\quad\ \ |\quad\ \ |\quad\ \ | \\
H-C-C-C-H \\
\quad\ \ |\quad\ \ |\quad\ \ | \\
\quad\ \ H\quad OH\ H
\end{array}
$$

C
$$
\begin{array}{c}
\quad\ \ H\quad OH\ H \\
\quad\ \ |\quad\ \ |\quad\ \ | \\
H-C-C-C-H \\
\quad\ \ |\quad\ \ |\quad\ \ | \\
\quad\ \ H\quad H\quad H
\end{array}
$$

B
$$
\begin{array}{c}
\quad\ \ H\quad H\quad H \\
\quad\ \ |\quad\ |\quad\ | \\
H-C-C-C-OH \\
\quad\ \ |\quad\ |\quad\ | \\
\quad\ \ H\quad CH_3\ H
\end{array}
$$

D
$$
\begin{array}{c}
\quad\ \ H\quad H\quad H\quad H \\
\quad\ \ |\quad\ |\quad\ |\quad\ | \\
H-C-C-C-C-OH \\
\quad\ \ |\quad\ |\quad\ |\quad\ | \\
\quad\ \ H\quad H\quad H\quad H
\end{array}
$$

12 When a protein is denatured, the protein molecule

    A   changes shape

    B   is polymerised

    C   is hydrolysed

    D   is neutralised.

13 Which of the following is not the gram formula mass of an alcohol?

	Gram formula mass
A	16
B	32
C	46
D	60

unit 3

14 Oxidation of 3-methylbutan-2-ol to form a ketone results in the alcohol

    A   not changing mass

    B   losing 2 g per mole

    C   gaining 2 g per mole

    D   gaining 16 g per mole.

15 Scientists have developed a calorie free fat by reacting sucrose, shown below, with fatty acid molecules.

How many fatty acid molecules can react with a molecule of sucrose?

    A   1

    B   3

    C   7

    D   8

16 In all reversible reactions, equilibrium is reached when

unit 3

    A   the concentrations of reactants and products are equal

    B   the concentrations of reactants and products are constant

    C   the rate of the forward reaction is higher than the reverse reaction

    D   the rate of the reverse reaction is higher than the forward reaction.

unit 3

17 In which of the following reactions is the atom economy for a desired product 100%?

    A $C_2H_4 + H_2 \rightarrow C_2H_6$

    B $CH_4 + 2O_2 \rightarrow CO_2 + 2H_2O$

    C $Ca + 2HCl \rightarrow CaCl_2 + H_2$

    D $CaCO_3 + H_2SO_4 \rightarrow CaSO_4 + H_2O + CO_2$

unit 3

18 A reducing agent

    A   gains electrons and is reduced

    B   loses electrons and is reduced

    C   gains electrons and is oxidised

    D   loses electrons and is oxidised.

unit 3

19 Xenon trioxide is an unstable compound that breaks down to form xenon gas.

    $XeO_3 + \_\_H^+ + \_\_e^- \rightarrow Xe + \_\_H_2O$

The numbers of H^+, e^- and H_2O required to balance this equation are

    A $3H^+$, $3e^-$, $3H_2O$

    B $6H^+$, $6e^-$, $6H_2O$

    C $6H^+$, $6e^-$, $3H_2O$

    D $3H^+$, $3e^-$, $6H_2O$.

20 A student requires $20\,cm^3$ of hydrochloric acid to be transferred from a $250\,cm^3$ standard flask to a conical flask.

Which of the following pieces of equipment would provide the most accurate way of doing this?

    A   Burette

    B   Pipette

    C   Beaker

    D   Measuring cylinder

[End of Section 1]

Section 2

Total marks: 80

Attempt **ALL** questions.

Write your answer clearly in the spaces provided in this paper. Additional space for answers and rough work is provided at the end of this paper. If you use this space you must clearly identify the question number you are attempting. Any rough work must be written in this space. You should score through your rough work when you have written your final copy.

MARKS

1 Glucuronic acid is a carboxylic acid derived from glucose, the simplest form of sugar in the human body.

The role of this acid in the body is to combine with toxins to make them more water soluble so that they can be eliminated from the body in urine.

$$\begin{array}{c} O \\ \parallel \\ \\ H \text{---} OH \\ HO \text{---} H \\ H \text{---} OH \\ H \text{---} OH \\ O \text{---} OH \end{array}$$

Glucuronic acid

a) **Explain fully** why glucuronic acid is very soluble in water.   2

b) Glucuronic acid is produced in the body from glucose.

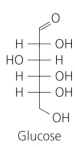

Glucose

(i) Name the type of reaction that takes place when glucose is converted to glucuronic acid.

1

(ii) Potassium gluconate, $C_6H_9O_7K$, a salt of glucuronic acid, can be taken as a mineral supplement.

Calculate the mass of potassium present in 5.99 g of potassium gluconate.

3

MARKS

2   The rate of a chemical reaction is a measure of how quickly reactants are converted into products.

Using your knowledge of chemistry, comment on what influences the rate at which the reactants are converted into products.

3

3 The enthalpy of combustion of methanol can be established by performing the experiment shown below.

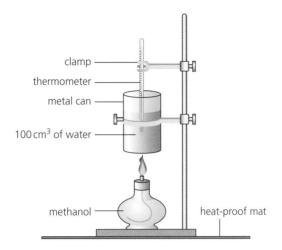

unit 3

a) Write the balanced equation corresponding to the enthalpy of combustion of methanol.

1

b) When the experiment was performed, it was found that 0.22 g of methanol resulted in the temperature of the water increasing from 15.0 °C to 24.2 °C.

Calculate the enthalpy of combustion, in kJ mol⁻¹, of methanol.

Show your working clearly.

3

c) The results obtained in this experiment are much lower than the figure quoted in the data booklet.

Suggest a reason why the results are lower than the data booklet value.

1

MARKS

4   Scientists have developed a method of using plants to generate isoprene, C_5H_8, in a process that is similar to photosynthesis.

a)   Draw the structural formula of isoprene.

1

b)   The isoprene generated in this process can be used as a biofuel.

$$C_5H_8 + 7O_2 \rightarrow 5CO_2 + 4H_2O$$

5 g of isoprene was reacted with 5 g of oxygen.
Show by calculation which reactant was in excess.
Show your working clearly.

3

c)   Many compounds used in fragrances are molecules consisting of joined isoprene units.

(i)   State the name that is given to molecules consisting of joined isoprene units.

1

(ii) These molecules are also found in essential oils.
State what is meant by the term 'essential oil'.

1

d) The apparatus shown can be used to determine the gram formula mass of volatile substances contained within essential oils.

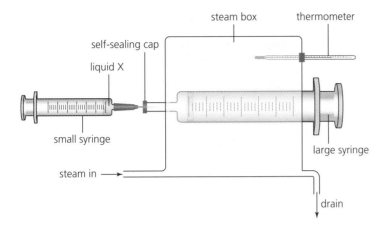

(i) Suggest why the experiment would only work with substances with a boiling point below 100 °C.

1

(ii) The experiment was carried out with 0.5 g of the unknown oil and 55 cm^3 of gas was collected in the syringe.

Calculate the gram formula mass of the unknown compound.

(Take the molar volume to be 24.1 litres mol^{-1}.)

Show your working clearly.

3

5 The table shown contains information on the ionisation energies of some alkali metals and halogens.

Element	Ionisation energies / kJ mol^{-1}		
	First	Second	Third
Sodium	496	4562	6910
Chlorine	1251	2298	3822
Potassium	419	3052	4420
Bromine	1140	2083	3473
Rubidium	403	2633	3859
Iodine	1008	1846	3184

a) Write the equation for the second ionisation of sodium.

1

b) **Explain fully** why the second ionisation energy of each alkali metal is much lower than that of a halogen in the same period.

2

c) **Explain fully** why the first ionisation energy of both alkali metals and halogens decreases as you move down their groups.

2

d) Calculate the energy required to change gaseous rubidium atoms to rubidium ions with a +3 charge.

2

6   During the 2016 Olympics in Rio, the pool used for the diving events changed colour from the normal blue colour to green. This was due to the addition of too much hydrogen peroxide that acted as a dechlorinating agent, removing the chlorine that had been added to the swimming pool, resulting in the growth of green algae.

$$Cl_2 + H_2O_2 \rightarrow O_2 + 2HCl$$

a)   (i)   Name the oxidising agent in the above reaction.   1

(ii)   Some divers stated that they suffered from more eye irritation that they would normally expect.

Suggest a reason for this.   1

(iii)   Approximately 232 kg of H_2O_2 was added to the pool in Rio.

Calculate the mass of chlorine, in kg, that this mass of hydrogen peroxide would remove from the pool.

Show your working clearly.   3

b) Chlorine is normally added to swimming pools in the form of sodium hypochlorite, NaClO, which dissolves in water to release sodium ions, chloride ions and hydroxyl free radicals.

$$NaClO + H_2O \rightarrow Na^+ + Cl^- + 2HO\bullet$$

(i) State what is meant by the term free radical.

1

(ii) The hydroxyl radicals can self-react to form water and oxygen. Write an equation for this reaction. There is no need to balance the equation.

1

c) The distinctive smell of swimming pools is caused by a chemical called nitrogen trichloride.

Nitrogen trichloride reacts with water to form ammonia and hypochlorous acid.

$$NCl_3(g) + H_2O(l) \rightarrow NH_3(aq) + HOCl(aq)$$

(i) Balance this equation.

1

(ii) Hypochlorous acid breaks down to form hydrochloric acid and oxygen. The rate of this reaction can be increased if copper oxide is added. The diagram below shows the change in potential energy during this reaction when carried out without copper oxide.

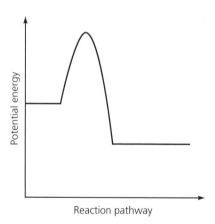

Reaction pathway

Add a line to the diagram to show the effect of adding copper oxide to the reaction.

1

7 Markovnikov's rule describes the outcome of some addition reactions.

'If a compound such as HBr or H_2O is added to an unsaturated compound, a hydrogen atom from the HBr or H_2O attaches to the carbon atom of the double bond that already has the most hydrogens directly attached to it to form the major product.

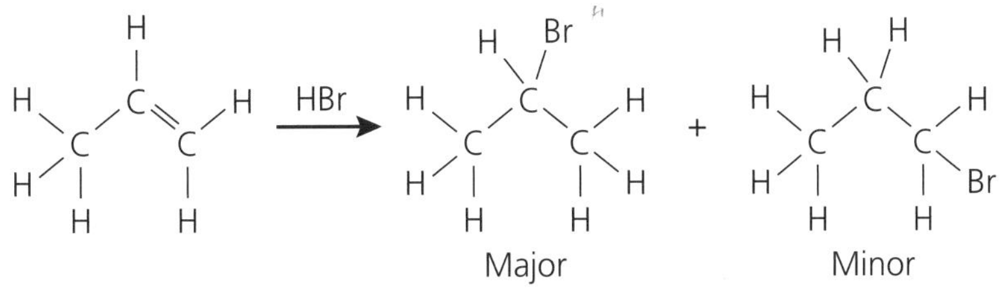

a) (i) Draw the full structural formula of the major compound formed when H_2O reacts with propene.

1

(ii) State the name of the compound produced when the major product of this reaction is oxidised.

1

b) Explain why it is not necessary to consider Markovnikov's rule when hydrogen bromide reacts with but-2-ene.

1

MARKS

c) Paper chromatography can also be used to identify the two products of these reactions.

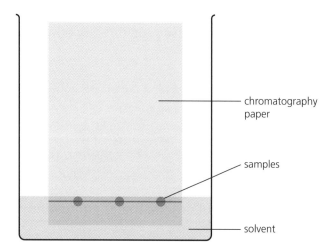

chromatography paper

samples

solvent

(i) State the two factors that affect how far compounds travel up the chromatography paper.

1

(ii) Suggest why the experiment shown has been set up incorrectly.

1

(iii) On a chromatogram, the retention factor Rf, for a substance can be calculated using the equation

$$Rf = \frac{\text{distance moved by compound}}{\text{maximum distance moved by the solvent}}$$

State which of the compounds in the chromatogram shown has the highest Rf value.

1

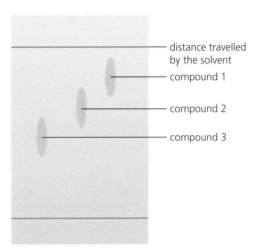

distance travelled by the solvent

compound 1

compound 2

compound 3

MARKS

8 The structure and bonding of elements and compounds can be established using the periodic table.

Using your knowledge of chemistry, comment on how the periodic table can be used to establish the bonding and structure of elements and compounds.

3

9 Esters such as methyl ethanoate have many uses.

   a) (i) Draw the full structural formula of methyl ethanoate.

1

   (ii) Esters such as methyl ethanoate can be used as flavourings for foods.
   State another use for methyl ethanoate.

1

   b) A student used 16 g of methanol, formula mass of 32 g, and excess ethanoic acid to produce 25 g of methyl ethanoate, formula mass 74 g.

$$CH_3OH + CH_3COOH \rightleftharpoons CH_3OOCCH_3 + H_2O$$

   (i) Calculate the percentage yield of methyl ethanoate.
   Show your working clearly.

3

   (ii) Suggest why a yield of 100% cannot be obtained in this reaction.

1

MARKS

c) Methyl ethanoate can be prepared in the laboratory using the following apparatus.

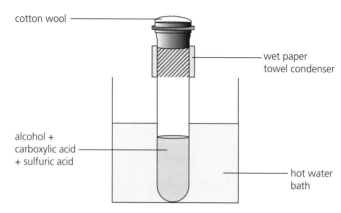

cotton wool

wet paper towel condenser

alcohol +
carboxylic acid
+ sulfuric acid

hot water bath

Suggest why a wet paper towel is wrapped around the test tube.

1

d) Name the type of reaction that takes place during the formation of methyl ethanoate.

1

A

MARKS

10 Heating cyclobutane in a closed system can cause the ring to open and form but-1-ene, resulting in the formation of an equilibrium.

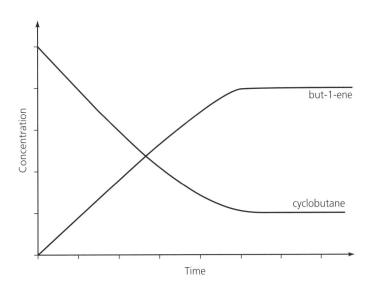

The graph shows the concentrations of cyclobutane and but-1-ene as equilibrium is established.

a) Mark on the graph the point at which equilibrium has been established.

1

b) Equilibrium can only be established in a closed system.
State what is meant by the term 'closed system'.

1

c) An increase in temperature favours the production of but-1-ene.
Suggest what this shows about the enthalpy change for the formation of but-1-ene.

1

d) Pressure has no effect on the position of equilibrium.
Suggest what this shows about the states of both chemicals.

1

e) The equilibrium can also be achieved by starting with but-1-ene.

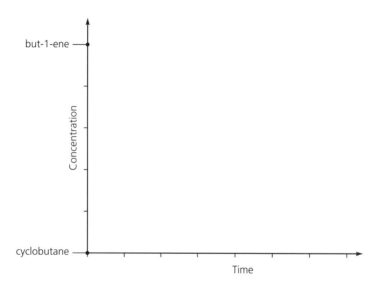

Using the initial concentrations shown, sketch two lines to show how the concentrations of but-1-ene and cyclobutane change as equilibrium is established.

1

A

unit 3
not done

11 Iron is a mineral that is naturally present in many foods, but is also added to some food products, and is available as a dietary supplement in the form of iron(II) sulfate.

The concentration of an iron(II) sulfate solution can be determined by performing a titration with acidified potassium permanganate.

$$5Fe^{2+}(aq) + MnO_4^-(aq) + 8H^+(aq) \rightarrow 5Fe^{3+}(aq) + Mn^{2+}(aq) + 4H_2O(l)$$

a) A standard solution of potassium permanganate is required to perform the titration.

   (i) State what is meant by the term 'standard solution'.

   1

   (ii) Describe fully how to prepare a standard solution of potassium permanganate.

   2

b) 20 cm³ iron(II) sulfate solution was titrated against 0.2 mol l⁻¹ potassium permanganate solution and the results recorded in the table shown.

Titration	Volume of potassium permanganate / cm³
1	9.1
2	8.8
3	8.7

Calculate the concentration, in mol l⁻¹, of the iron(II) sulfate solution.
Show your working clearly.

   3

c) During the reaction the permanganate ion is reduced to manganese. Complete the ion electron equation for the reduction of the permanganate ion.

1

$$MnO_4^-(aq) \rightarrow Mn^{2+}(aq)$$

d) The recommended intake of iron per day for a 14-year-old girl is 14 mg per day.

Canned tuna provides 2.7 mg of iron per 85 g of tuna.

Calculate the percentage of the recommended daily intake provided by 100 g of tuna.

Show your working clearly.

2

12 Protein supplements are taken by athletes to provide the essential amino acids that are needed to build muscle tissue quicker and more efficiently.

a) **(i)** State what is meant by the term 'essential amino acid'.

1

(ii) **Explain fully** why consuming protein in the diet can provide the body with essential amino acids.

2

b) Some scientists believe that protein supplements are not required as the quantity of protein required by the body is provided by a balanced diet.

Eggs are a good source of protein but during the cooking process the proteins contained in egg become denatured as the protein chains unwind, and the egg white solidifies.

Explain why the protein chains unwind.

1

c) Water-soluble proteins such as haemoglobin are called globular proteins.

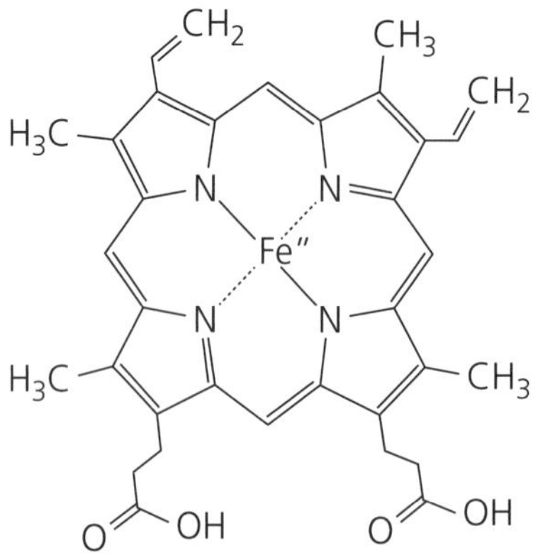

Explain with reference to its structure why haemoglobin is a soluble protein.

MARKS

1

d) Haemoglobin is also an example of a complex ion. A complex ion has a metal ion at its centre with a number of other molecules or ions surrounding it.

In haemoglobin the iron at the centre has a co-ordination number of four.

Another complex ion involving iron is hexaaquairon(II).

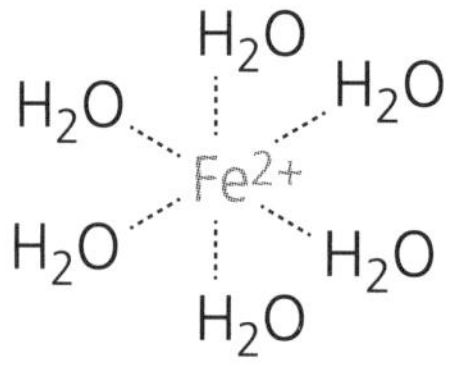

Give the co-ordination number of iron in the complex ion hexaaquairon(II).

1

e) Proteins called enzymes can be used to catalyse the breakdown of hydrogen peroxide into water and oxygen as shown by the following equation

$$2H_2O_2(aq) \rightarrow 2H_2O(l) + O_2(g)$$

The bond enthalpy of an oxygen-to-oxygen single bond is $142\,kJ\,mol^{-1}$. Use this information and the bond enthalpy values given in the data booklet to calculate the enthalpy change, in kJ, for the reaction.

Show your working clearly.

3

[END OF PRACTICE PAPER A]

ADDITIONAL SPACE FOR ANSWERS AND ROUGH WORK

Higher
Chemistry

B

Reference may be made to the Chemistry Higher and Advanced Higher Data Booklet.

Duration – 2 hours and 30 minutes

Total marks – 100

SECTION 1 – 20 marks

Attempt ALL questions.

SECTION 2 – 80 marks

Attempt ALL questions

Write your answers clearly in the spaces provided in this paper. Additional space for answers and rough work is provided at the end of this paper. If you use this space you must clearly identify the question number you are attempting. Any rough work must be written in this space. You should score through your rough work when you have written your final copy.

Use **blue** or **black** ink.

Section 1

Total marks: 20

Attempt **ALL** questions. Answer grid available at www.hoddereducation.co.uk/updatesandextras.

1 Which of the following bonds is only found in elements?

    A Ionic bond

    B Polar covalent

    C Hydrogen bond

    D Non-polar covalent bond

2 Which of the following compounds would be the most polar?

    A HF

    B HCl

    C HBr

    D HI

3 Shown below is the energy profile for a chemical reaction.

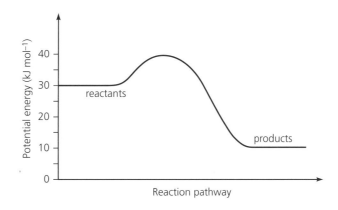

What is the activation energy, in $kJ\,mol^{-1}$, for the reverse reaction?

    A 10

    B 20

    C 30

    D 40

4 The melting points of the halogens are shown in the table.

Halogen	Melting point / °C
Fluorine	−220
Chlorine	−101
Bromine	−7
Iodine	114

The increase in melting point as you go down the halogen group is due to

A an increase in the strength of London dispersion forces

B a decrease in covalent radius

C a decrease in nuclear charge

D an increase in electronegativity.

5 Which of the following represents the third ionisation enthalpy of aluminium?

A $Al(s) \rightarrow Al^{3+}(s) + 3e^-$

B $Al^{2+}(s) \rightarrow Al^{3+}(s) + e^-$

C $Al(g) \rightarrow Al^{3+}(g) + 3e^-$

D $Al^{2+}(g) \rightarrow Al^{3+}(g) + e^-$

6 The graph shows how the rate of reaction changes as the concentration of one of the reactants is increased.

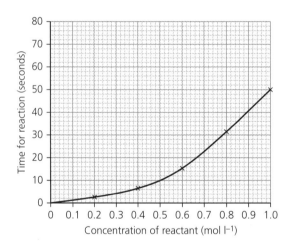

What was the rate, in s^{-1}, when the concentration of the reactant was $1.0\,mol\,l^{-1}$?

A 0.02

B 0.5

C 1

D 50

7

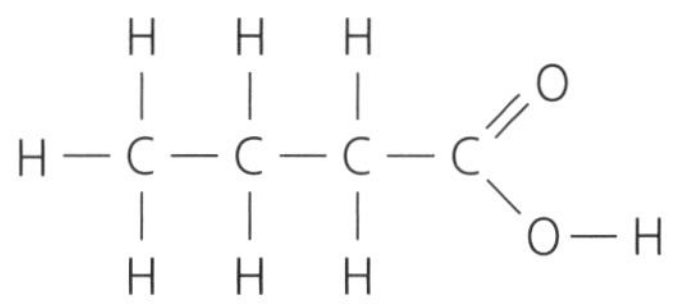

Which of the following compounds is an isomer of the structure shown?

A Butanal

B Butanol

C 2-Methylpropan-2-ol

D Methyl propanoate

8 The compound shown below is an example of

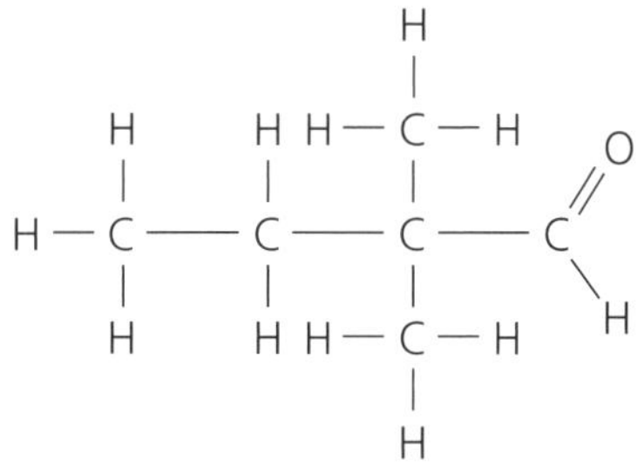

A a primary alcohol

B a carboxylic acid

C an aldehyde

D a ketone.

9 Which of the following can be classified as a salt?

A Soap

B Protein

C Alcohol

D Terpene

10 Which of the following class of compounds are not produced by a condensation reaction?

A Esters

B Fats

C Proteins

D Amino acids

11 $C_6H_8O_6(aq) + I_2(aq) \rightarrow C_6H_6O_6(aq) + 2H^+(aq) + 2I^-(aq)$

In the equation shown, which substance is acting as an antioxidant?

A $C_6H_8O_6$

B I_2

C $C_6H_6O_6$

D $2I^-$

12 Emulsifiers can be produced by reacting oils edible with

A fats

B esters

C glycerol

D carboxylic acids.

13 The equations shown below show the reaction of metals with metal oxides.

$$Mg(s) + FeO(s) \rightarrow MgO(s) + Fe(s) \qquad \Delta H = \mathbf{A}\,kJ\,mol^{-1}$$

$$Fe(s) + CuO(s) \rightarrow FeO(s) + Cu(s) \qquad \Delta H = \mathbf{B}\,kJ\,mol^{-1}$$

$$Mg(s) + CuO(s) \rightarrow MgO(s) + Cu(s) \qquad \Delta H = \mathbf{C}\,kJ\,mol^{-1}$$

Which is the correct relationship between A, B and C according to Hess's Law?

A C + A = −B

B C + A = B

C A + B = −C

D A + B = C

14 The balanced equation for the combustion of butane is shown.

$$2C_4H_{10}(g) + 13O_2(g) \rightarrow 8CO_2(g) + 10H_2O(l)$$

What volume of oxygen, in litres, is required to react with 1 mole of butane?
Take molar volume to be $24\,l\,mol^{-1}$.

A 24

B 48

C 156

D 312

15 Industrial processes are always designed to minimise the impact on the environment. Which of the following is **not** an environmental factor influencing process design?

A Minimising waste

B Marketability of by-products

C Avoiding the use of toxic chemicals

D Designing products that will biodegrade if possible

16 Which of the following techniques uses differences in polarity and/or size of molecules to separate components within a mixture?

A Volumetric analysis

B Gravimetric analysis

C Chromatography

D Redox titration

17 An oxidising agent

    A   loses electrons and is reduced

    B   gains electrons and is reduced

    C   loses electrons and is oxidised

    D   gains electrons and is oxidised.

18 Which of the following equations does not represent the enthalpy of combustion of an alcohol?

    A $CH_3OH + 1\tfrac{1}{2}O_2 \rightarrow CO_2 + 2H_2O$

    B $2C_2H_5OH + 6O_2 \rightarrow 4CO_2 + 6H_2O$

    C $C_3H_7OH + 4\tfrac{1}{2}O_2 \rightarrow 3CO_2 + 4H_2O$

    D $C_4H_9OH + 6O_2 \rightarrow 4CO_2 + 5H_2O$

19

$$2IO_3^- + \underline{\ \ }H^+ + \underline{\ \ }e^- \rightarrow I_2 + \underline{\ \ }H_2O$$

The numbers of H^+, e^- and H_2O required to balance this equation are

    A $6H^+$, $5e^-$, $3H_2O$

    B $12H^+$, $10e^-$, $6H_2O$

    C $12H^+$, $10e^-$, $3H_2O$

    D $6H^+$, $5e^-$, $6H_2O$.

20 An indicator is a substance which changes colour at the end-point of a chemical reaction. The pH range of an indicator is the pH at which the indicator will change colour.

The pH ranges of some indicators are shown below.

Indicator	pH range
Trapaeolin	1.3–3.0
Bromophenol blue	3.0–4.6
Phenol red	6.8–8.4
Metacresol purple	7.6–9.2

Which indicator would be the most suitable for a titration between hydrochloric acid and sodium hydroxide?

    A   Trapaeolin

    B   Bromophenol blue

    C   Phenol red

    D   Metacresol purple

[End of Section 1]

Section 2

Total marks: 80

Attempt **ALL** questions.

Write your answer clearly in the spaces provided in this paper. Additional space for answers and rough work is provided at the end of this paper. If you use this space you must clearly identify the question number you are attempting. Any rough work must be written in this space. You should score through your rough work when you have written your final copy.

MARKS

1 Krypton difluoride, KrF_2, was the first compound containing the element krypton to be discovered.

It can be prepared directly from its constituent elements as shown by the equation:

$$Kr + F_2 \rightarrow KrF_2 \qquad \Delta H = -193 \, kJ \, mol^{-1}$$

a) The krypton required for this process is extracted from liquid air.

(i) Suggest how the krypton could be extracted from the liquid air.   1

(ii) Air contains about 0.00011% krypton.
Calculate the volume of air that would be required to produce 1 litre of krypton.   2

b) Using your data booklet, calculate the mean bond enthalpy, in $kJ\,mol^{-1}$, of the Kr–F bond in KrF_2.
Show your working clearly.

3

c) Krypton difluoride can react with silver atoms. The overall reaction is shown in the equation:

$$3KrF_2 + 2Ag \rightarrow 2AgF_3 + 3Kr$$

(i) Write the ion-electron equation for the oxidation reaction.

1

(ii) Name the oxidising agent in the reaction shown.

1

2   The table below gives information on four different covalent substances.

Formula	CH_4	NH_3	SO_2	SiO_2
Formula mass	16	17	64.1	60.1
Boiling point / °C	−162	−33	−10	2950
Solubility in water	Insoluble	Very soluble	Very soluble	Insoluble

a) **Explain fully** why, although methane and ammonia have very similar formula masses, they have very different properties.

In your answer, you should mention intermolecular forces and how they arise.

3

b) State why the melting point of silicon dioxide is significantly higher than sulfur dioxide.

1

3 Vitamin C is an essential nutrient for humans.

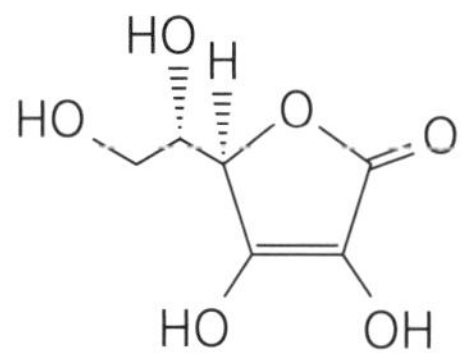

a) **Explain fully** why vitamin C is soluble in water.

2

b) Iodine solution reacts with vitamin C according to the equation:

$$C_6H_8O_6(aq) + I_2(aq) \rightarrow C_6H_6O_6(aq) + 2H^+(aq) + 2I^-(aq)$$
$$\text{(brown)} \qquad\qquad\qquad \text{(colourless)}$$

A titration was performed using 25 cm³ of 0.2 mol l⁻¹ vitamin C solution added to 1 g of iodine in solution.

(i) Show by calculation which reactant is in excess.
Show your working clearly.

3

(ii) If the reaction went to completion, suggest why no indicator is required.

1

B

(iii) The vitamin C used in the reaction was taken from a standard solution.

Describe how to prepare a standard solution if you have been given the correct mass of vitamin C powder.

c) When iodine is dissolved in water the following equilibrium is established:

$$I_2(aq) + H_2O(l) \rightleftharpoons 2H^+(aq) + I^-(aq) + IO^-(aq)$$

Explain fully the effect that adding potassium hydroxide would have on the position of equilibrium.

4 All chemical changes are accompanied by the absorption or release of heat and this can be used to predict the energy changes associated with chemical processes.

Using your knowledge of chemistry, comment on why energy is an important consideration in any chemical process.

3

MARKS

5 Tartaric acid is found naturally in many fruits including grapes.

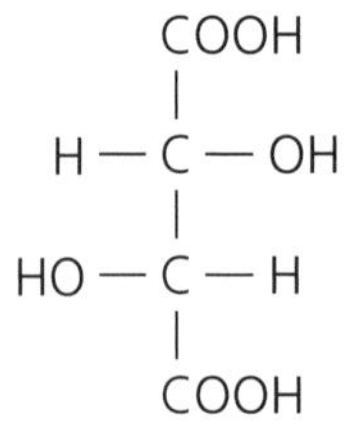

$$
\begin{array}{c}
COOH \\
| \\
H-C-OH \\
| \\
HO-C-H \\
| \\
COOH
\end{array}
$$

a) Name the two functional groups present in tartaric acid.

1

b) Tartaric acid can be used to prepare esters.
(i) State the number of moles of alcohol that can react with one mole of tartaric acid.

1

(ii) Name the type of reaction that takes place between tartaric acid and an alcohol.

1

c) An ester of tartaric acid called DATEM is used as an emulsifier in foods. State the role of an emulsifier in foods.

1

d) An ester found in grapes is ethyl nonanoate. It can be produced in the lab using ethanol and nonanoic acid.

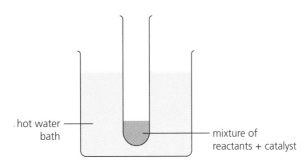

(i) Suggest why a water bath and not a Bunsen burner must be used to heat the reaction mixture.

1

(ii) Suggest why the reaction mixture must be kept at a temperature below 78°C.

1

(iii) The equation for the reaction is shown below.

$$C_2H_5OH + CH_3(CH_2)_7COOH \rightleftharpoons CH_3(CH_2)_6CH_2 \overset{O}{\underset{}{\parallel}} C\text{--}O\text{--}CH_3 + H_2O$$

If there is a 65% yield, calculate the mass of ester (gram formula mass of 186 g) produced, in grams, from 23 g of alcohol.
Show your working clearly.

3

6   Cosmetic chemists are responsible for testing and developing ingredients that improve the appearance and health of skin. These ingredients are derived from a vast array of raw materials – the Personal Care Products Council lists over 10 000 raw materials.

Using your knowledge of chemistry, comment on the ingredients present in cosmetics and the reason they are added.

3

7 A mixture of chemicals and additives that included large quantities of benzene, alcohols and aviation fuel fuelled early Grand Prix cars.

a) The structure of one of the hydrocarbons found in aviation fuel is shown.

$$H - C - C - C - C - C - H$$

(i) Give the systematic name of this hydrocarbon.

1

MARKS

(ii) The energy released when this hydrocarbon (gram formula mass of 114 g) burns can be established by performing the experiment shown.

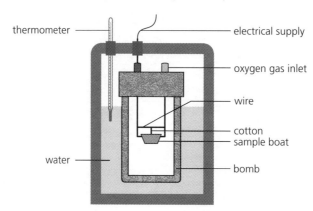

thermometer — electrical supply — oxygen gas inlet — wire — cotton — sample boat — bomb — water

It was found that the hydrocarbon has an enthalpy of combustion of $-5460\,kJ\,mol^{-1}$.

Calculate the change in temperature of the water, in °C, if 1 gram of the fuel was used to heat $500\,cm^3$ of water.

Show your working clearly.

3

(iii) Suggest why the results obtained using this equipment are higher than those achieved in the classroom.

1

b) When benzene was first discovered it was suggested that it had the structure shown.

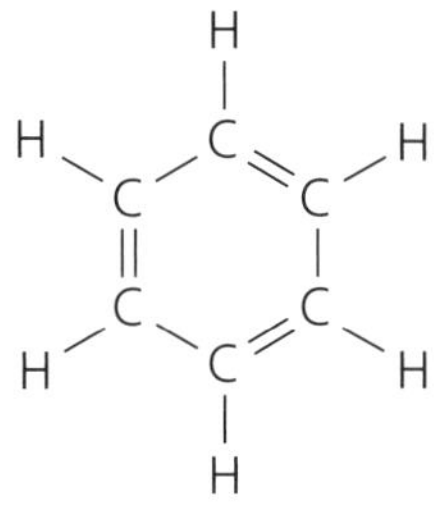

(i) Write the molecular formula of benzene.

1

(ii) In lab tests it was proven that benzene does not contain double bonds.

Suggest a test that could be performed, including results, which would prove that benzene does not contain a double bond.

1

(iii) The equation for the formation of benzene from carbon and hydrogen is shown below.

$$6C(s) + 3H_2(g) \rightarrow C_6H_6(l)$$

Use the enthalpies of combustion from your data booklet to calculate the enthalpy of formation, in $kJ\,mol^{-1}$, of benzene.

Show your working clearly.

3

c) Some modern cars are powered by fuel cells. Fuel cells generate electricity by chemical means.

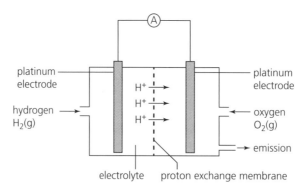

(i) The ion-electron equations, which occur at each electrode, are shown.

$$H_2(g) \rightarrow 2H^+(aq) + 2e^-$$

$$O_2(g) + 4H^+ + 4e^- \rightarrow 2H_2O(l)$$

Combine the two ion-electron equations to give the overall redox equation.

1

(ii) Suggest why fuel cells are thought to be more environmentally friendly than aviation fuels.

1

8 The table below gives the covalent radius and ionisation values of some Group 1 elements.

Element	Covalent radius / pm	First ionisation energy / kJ mol^{-1}	Second ionisation energy / kJ mol^{-1}
Lithium	134	520	7298
Sodium	154	496	4562
Potassium	196	419	3052
Rubidium	216	403	2633
Caesium	235	376	2234

a) **Explain fully** why the covalent radius increases as you move down a group of the periodic table.

2

b) State the link between covalent radius and the first ionisation energy.

1

c) Write the ion-electron equation corresponding to the second ionisation energy of caesium.

1

d) **Explain fully** why there is such a large increase in energy between the first and second ionisation energy of all the Group 1 elements.

2

e) Electronegativity also shows a regular change going down Group 1.
   (i) State what is meant by the term electronegativity.

1

   (ii) **Explain fully** why electronegativity decreases going down Group 1.

2

9 According to Roman legend, soap got its name from Mount Sapo, an area where animals were sacrificed. Rain would wash the fat from the sacrificed animals along with alkaline wooden ashes from the sacrificial fires into the Tiber River, where people found the resulting mixture helped to clean clothes.

a) State the name of the reaction that took place between the fat and alkaline wooden ashes.

1

b) **Explain fully** how soaps remove grease stains from clothes.

2

c) State why the use of detergents rather than soaps is recommended in hard water areas.

1

10 Malachite (copper hydroxide carbonate) is a mineral containing copper ions. It decomposes completely when heated to 200°C.

$$Cu(OH)_2CuCO_3(s) \rightarrow 2CuO(s) + CO_2(g) + H_2O(g)$$

(Formula mass = 221 g)

This can be performed in the lab as shown:

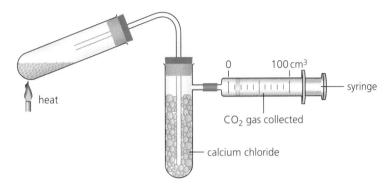

a) Suggest why calcium chloride is required.

1

b) When the reaction was complete the volume of carbon dioxide collected was 56 cm³.
Calculate the mass, in grams, of malachite added to the test tube.
Take the molar volume of a gas to be 24 litres mol⁻¹.

3

c) The copper(II) oxide produced in this reaction can be used to produce copper metal by reacting it with carbon monoxide

$$CuO + CO \rightarrow Cu + CO_2$$

(i) Name the reducing agent in the reaction shown.

1

(ii) Calculate the atom economy of this reaction.

2

(iii) The collision theory states that for the two compounds to react they must collide. State **two** factors that are required for a successful collision to take place.

1

11 Enzymes are protein molecules that are manufactured by all plants and animals.

a) State the name of the functional group that all proteins contain. 1

b) Dietary enzymes break down proteins to form amino acids such as the essential amino acid valine.

(i) State the name of the reaction that occurs when proteins are broken down to form amino acids. 1

(ii) Draw the structure of the molecule produced when two valine molecules combine. 1

(iii) State what is meant by the term 'essential amino acid'. 1

c) When proteins are heated during cooking, they are denatured.
Explain fully what happens when a protein is denatured. 2

d) Catalase is an enzyme contained in potatoes. Catalase catalyses the decomposition of hydrogen peroxide.

$$H_2O_2(aq) \rightarrow H_2O(l) + O_2(g)$$

A student recorded the volume of oxygen gas recorded at various temperatures by performing the experiment shown.

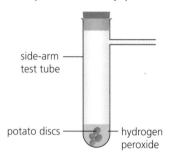

(i) Complete the diagram to show how the volume of oxygen gas produced could be measured.

1

(ii) The results recorded were used to create the rate graph shown.

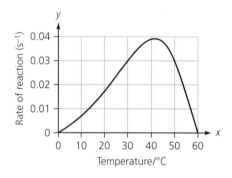

Calculate the time, in s, for the reaction at 30°C.

1

12 Propene can react with a mixture of carbon monoxide and hydrogen in the presence of a cobalt catalyst to form an aldehyde and a ketone.

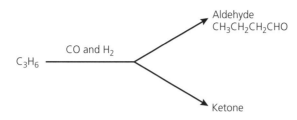

MARKS

a) Draw the full structural formula of the ketone formed in this reaction.

1

b) State the name of a reagent that could be used to distinguish between the aldehyde and ketone.

1

c) Reacting an alcohol with a mild oxidising agent can also produce aldehydes and ketones.
State the type of alcohol which produces an aldehyde on oxidation.

1

[END OF PRACTICE PAPER B]

ADDITIONAL SPACE FOR ANSWERS AND ROUGH WORK

Higher Chemistry

Reference may be made to the Chemistry Higher and Advanced Higher Data Booklet.

Duration – 2 hours and 30 minutes

Total marks – 100

SECTION 1 – 20 marks

Attempt ALL questions.

SECTION 2 – 80 marks

Attempt ALL questions

Write your answers clearly in the spaces provided in this paper. Additional space for answers and rough work is provided at the end of this paper. If you use this space you must clearly identify the question number you are attempting. Any rough work must be written in this space. You should score through your rough work when you have written your final copy.

Use **blue** or **black** ink.

Section 1

Total marks: 20

Attempt **ALL** questions. Answer grid available at www.hoddereducation.co.uk/updatesandextras.

1 A negatively charged particle with the electron arrangement of 2,8,8 could be

   A   an argon atom

   B   a chloride ion

   C   a fluoride ion

   D   a potassium ion.

2 Which of the following equations represents the first ionisation energy of oxygen?

   A $O_2(g) \rightarrow 2O^{2+}(g) + 2e^-$

   B $O_2(g) + 2e^- \rightarrow 2O^{2+}(g)$

   C $O(g) \rightarrow O^+(g) + e^-$

   D $O(g) \rightarrow O^-(g) + e^-$

3 An excess of calcium carbonate was added to $50\,cm^3$ of $1\,mol\,l^{-1}$ sulfuric acid.

Which measurement, when recorded at regular time intervals, would produce the graph shown below?

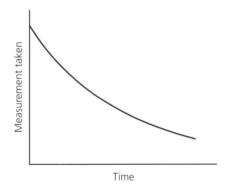

   A   Volume of gas produced

   B   pH of solution

   C   Temperature change

   D   Mass of beaker and contents

4 Which types of bond are at opposite ends of the bonding continuum?

   A   van der Waals and pure covalent

   B   Pure covalent and ionic

   C   Polar covalent and ionic

   D   Polar covalent and pure covalent

5 Which of the following elements has the greatest attraction for electrons in a covalent bond?

  A Nitrogen **C** Fluorine

  B Oxygen **D** Chlorine

6 Which of the following is the correct structure of isoprene?

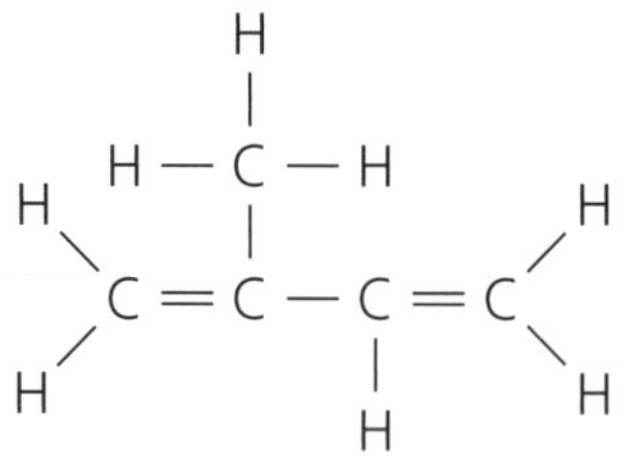

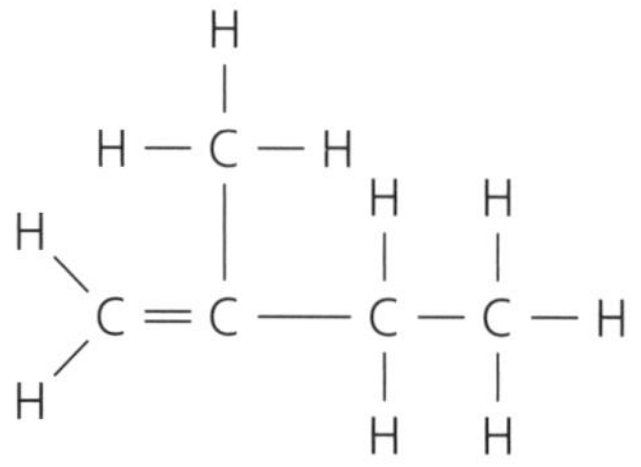

7 Vegetable oils, such as sunflower oil, can be converted to fats.

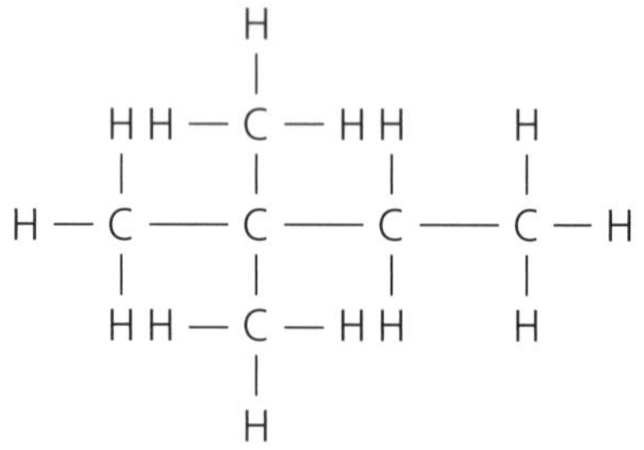

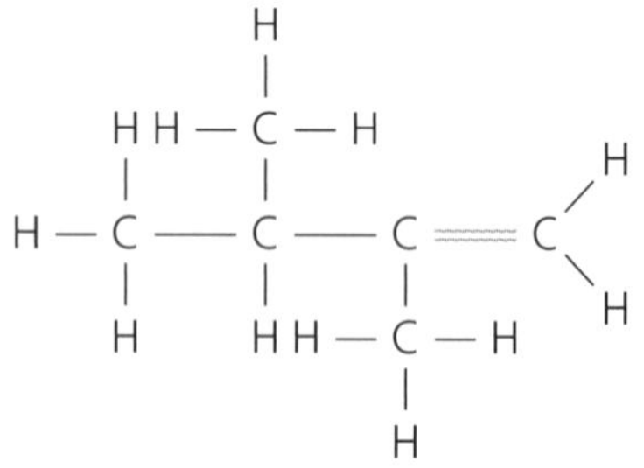

Which of the following is the type of reaction that converts oils to fats?

  A Hydrolysis

  B Condensation

  C Hydrogenation

  D Dehydrogenation

8 Propane-1,2,3-triol is also known as

  A glycerol

  B fullerene

  C aldehyde

  D ketone.

9   Which of the following would **not** react with acidified potassium dichromate?

   A   Butan-1-ol

   B   Butan-2-ol

   C   2-methylbutan-1-ol

   D   2-methylbutan-2-ol

10 Enzyme molecules can be classified as

   A   esters

   B   fats

   C   alcohols

   D   proteins.

11 A positive test for an aldehyde using Fehling's reagent would be indicated by which colour change?

   A   Green to orange

   B   Blue to brick red

   C   Silver mirror formed

   D   Black to brown

12 Which of the following correctly states the effect that adding a catalyst will have on a reaction mixture at equilibrium?

   A   The position of equilibrium is unchanged.

   B   The ΔH of the reverse reaction will increase.

   C   The ΔH of the forward reaction will increase.

   D   The position of equilibrium always shifts to the right.

13 During a redox process, chlorate ions are converted into chlorine.

$$ClO_3^- \rightarrow Cl_2$$

The reaction is carried out in acidic conditions to provide H^+ ions.

The number of H^+ ions required to balance this ion–electron equation is

   A   6

   B   8

   C   10

   D   12.

14 In which of the following reactions would a change in pressure **not** affect the yield of product?

   A $ICl(l) + Cl_2(g) \rightarrow ICl_3(s)$

   B $2NO_2(g) \rightarrow N_2O_4(g)$

   C $H_2(g) + I_2(g) \rightarrow 2HI(g)$

   D $N_2(g) + 3H_2(g) \rightarrow 2NH_3(g)$

15 The equation for the complete combustion of methane is shown below.

$$CH_4(g) + 2O_2(g) \rightarrow CO_2(g) + 2H_2O(l)$$

If $10\,cm^3$ of methane is ignited and burned with $50\,cm^3$ of oxygen what is the volume of the resulting gas mixture?

A $10\,cm^3$

B $20\,cm^3$

C $30\,cm^3$

D $40\,cm^3$

16 Consider the reaction pathway shown below.

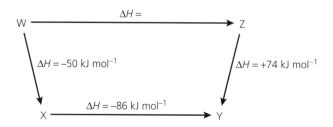

According to Hess's law, the ΔH value, in $kJ\,mol^{-1}$, for reaction W to Z is

A −62

B +62

C −210

D +210.

17

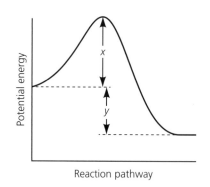

The enthalpy change for the forward reaction can be represented by

A x

B y

C x-y

D x+y.

18 Which of the following could be used to oxidise bromide ions to bromine?

$$2Br^-(aq) \rightarrow Br_2(l) + 2e^-$$

A $Cr_2O_7^{2-}(aq)$

B $Hg^{2+}(aq)$

C $SO_4^{2-}(aq)$

D $Fe^{3+}(aq)$

19 Which of the following can be classed as a redox reaction?

A $Mg + 2HCl \rightarrow MgCl_2 + H_2$

B $NiO + 2HCl \rightarrow NiCl_2 + H_2O$

C $KOH + HCl \rightarrow KCl + H_2O$

D $CuCO_3 + 2HCl \rightarrow CuCl_2 + CO_2 + H_2O$

20 The results of a titration experiment are recorded in the table below.

Titre	Start volume / cm^3	Final volume / cm^3	Total volume / cm^3
1	0.0	10.7	10.7
2	11.0	21.1	10.1
3	22.0	32.4	10.4
4	33.0	43.0	10.0

What is the average titre, in cm^3, that should be used?

A 10.05

B 10.17

C 10.20

D 10.30

[End of Section 1]

C

Section 2

MARKS

1 Stannic chloride ($SnCl_4$) was used in World War I as a chemical weapon due to its corrosive and toxic properties. It can be produced by the reaction shown.

$$HgCl_2(s) + SnCl_2(s) \rightarrow Hg(l) + SnCl_4(l)$$

    a)   State the type of bonding and structure in stannic chloride.   1

    b)   Write the equation for the oxidation step in this reaction.   1

    c)   Calculate the atom economy of the reaction.   3

d) Stannic chloride has a density of $2.2\,g\,cm^{-3}$.

Suggest how the stannic chloride could be separated from the mercury.

You may wish to use your data booklet to help you.

1

e) During the war, food shortages led to a recommendation that people should eat rhubarb leaves.

However, this resulted in several poisonings because rhubarb leaves are relatively high in oxalic acid.

The number of moles of oxalic acid in a dissolved sample can be established by titrating with a solution of potassium permanganate solution.

$5(COOH)_2(aq) + 6H^+(aq) + 2MnO_4^-(aq) \rightarrow 2Mn^{2+}(aq) + 10CO_2(g) + 8H_2O(l)$
  oxalic acid

(i) Suggest why no indicator is required to identify the endpoint of the reaction.

1

(ii) A titration was performed on 25 cm³ of the dissolved sample using 0.04 mol l⁻¹ potassium permanganate. The following results were obtained.

Titration	Volume of potassium permanganate solution used / cm³
1	27.7
2	26.8
3	27.4
4	27.0

Calculate the average volume of potassium permanganate, in cm³, that should be used in further calculations.

1

(iii) Calculate the number of moles of oxalic acid that would be contained in 100 cm³ of the dissolved sample.

3

f) A lethal dose of oxalic acid can be as low as 15 g.

Calculate the mass of rhubarb leaves that would have to be consumed if the average mass, in grams, of oxalic acid contained in the leaves is 0.52 g per 100 g.

1

2 Guaifenesin and acetaminophen are ingredients in cough bottles.

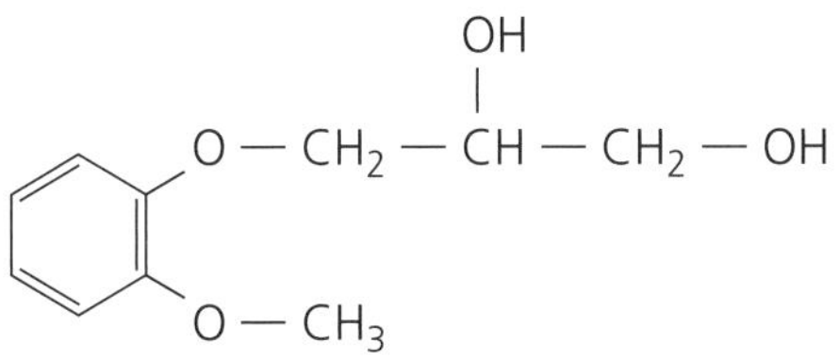

Guaifenesin 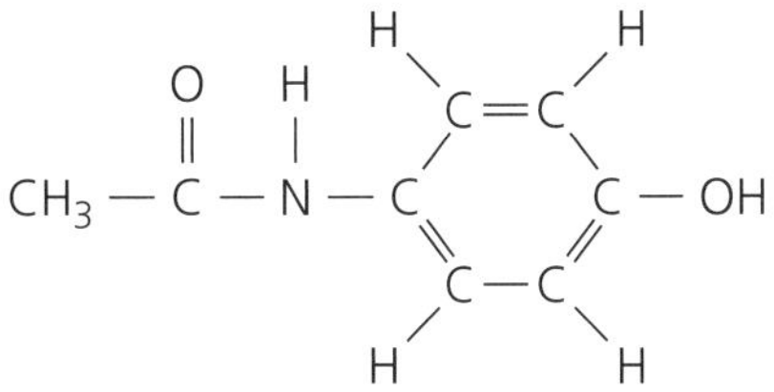   **Acetaminophen**

a) **Explain fully** why both guaifenesin and acetaminophen are water soluble.

2

b) Name the two oxygen-containing functional groups contained in acetaminophen.

1

c) Drugs containing acetaminophen should be stored at room temperature away from moisture.

Suggest why they should be stored in this way.

1

3   Various chemical analysis techniques can be used to help identify chemicals present in reaction mixtures or give important information about the products of a chemical reaction.

Using your knowledge of chemistry, comment on chemical analysis techniques used in the lab to identify the reactants or products of a chemical reaction.

3

4 Copper metal can react with concentrated sulfuric acid, according to the following equation:

$$Cu(s) + 2H_2SO_4(aq) \rightarrow SO_2(g) + CuSO_4(aq) + 2H_2O(l)$$

a) The reaction is slow at room temperature, but heating the mixture can increase the rate.

Explain fully why increasing the temperature increases the rate of the reaction.

2

b) (i) Sulfur dioxide is very soluble in water. Complete the diagram to show how the sulfur dioxide produced in the experiment could be collected and the volume measured.

1

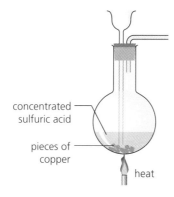

concentrated sulfuric acid

pieces of copper

heat

(ii) When the reaction was complete, 45 cm³ of sulfur dioxide was collected. Calculate the mass, in grams, of copper that reacted.

Take molar volume to be 24 litres mol⁻¹.

Show your working clearly.

3

C

5 Weak acids partially break up into ions to form an equilibrium when dissolved in water. An example of this occurs in nature when sulfur dioxide dissolves in rain water to form sulfurous acid, which is the major cause of acid rain.

$$SO_2(aq) + H_2O(l) \rightleftharpoons 2H^+(aq) + SO_3^{2-}(aq)$$

a) Circle the correct words in the table below to show what is true for reactions at equilibrium.

Rate of forward reaction compared to rate of the reverse reaction	faster / slower / equal
Concentration of the reactants compared to the products	equal / usually different

2

b) Any equilibrium can be described in terms of the equilibrium constant, K. From the following reaction at equilibrium

$$aA + bB \rightleftharpoons cC + dD$$

the equilibrium constant is given by:

$$K = \frac{[C]^c[D]^d}{[A]^a[B]^b}$$

Use this information to write the equation for the equilibrium constant for the production of sulfurous acid.

1

c) Strong acids break up completely into ions when dissolved in water.

$$H_2SO_4(aq) \rightarrow 2H^+(aq) + SO_4^{2-}(aq)$$

	Strong acid $H_2SO_4(aq)$ (1 mol l^{-1})	Weak acid $H_2SO_3(aq)$ (1 mol l^{-1})
Volume needed to neutralise 40 cm^3 of 1 mol l^{-1} NaOH	20 cm^3	20 cm^3

Explain fully, with reference to equilibrium, why 20 cm^3 of each acid requires the same volume of alkali to neutralise it.

3

6   Chocolate is approximately 40% fat due to the cocoa butter contained in the chocolate. The cocoa butter provides most of the flavour and colour. Cocoa butter is composed of three fatty acids.

Fatty acid	Melting point / °C	Class of fatty acid
Palmitic acid	63	Saturated
Stearic acid	63	Saturated
Oleic acid	14	Unsaturated

a)   Fatty acids are obtained on hydrolysis of a fat or oil. Name the other product of this reaction.

1

b)   **Explain fully** why the melting point of oils containing oleic acid is lower than fats composed of both palmitic and stearic acids.

2

c)   State the name of the reaction that converts oils to fats.

1

d) Iodine solution can be used to test for the degree of unsaturation of oils because it adds across any carbon to carbon double bonds in the oil molecule.

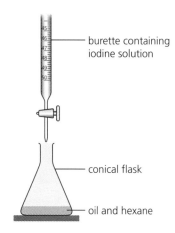

burette containing
iodine solution

conical flask

oil and hexane

    (i) Describe fully how this apparatus could be used to show the degree of unsaturation of an oil.

2

    (ii) Suggest why hexane is used as the solvent, rather than water.

1

7 Butanal and butanone both contain the same functional group despite being members of different homologous series.

a) Name the functional group present in both butanal and butanone. 1

b) Describe a chemical test including result that could be used to distinguish butanal from butanone. 1

c) The equation for the formation of butanone is

$$4C(s) + 4H_2(g) + \tfrac{1}{2}O_2(g) \rightarrow C_4H_8O(l)$$

Use the following information to calculate the enthalpy of formation of butanone. 2

$$C(s) + O_2(g) \rightarrow CO_2(g) \qquad\qquad \Delta H = -394\,kJ\,mol^{-1}$$

$$H_2(g) + \tfrac{1}{2}O_2(g) \rightarrow H_2O(l) \qquad\qquad \Delta H = -286\,kJ\,mol^{-1}$$

$$C_4H_8O(l) + 5\tfrac{1}{2}O_2(g) \rightarrow 4CO_2(g) + 4H_2O(l) \qquad\qquad \Delta H = -2444\,kJ\,mol^{-1}$$

C

8 In ancient Egypt the mummification process involved several steps. The first step involved adding compounds containing sodium to the body cavity, which removed water and also resulted in the saponification of fats, preventing decay.

a) Saponification is the reaction of fats with an alkali to form soaps.

   (i) State another name for this reaction.

          1

   (ii) Explain fully how soaps remove grease stains.

          2

b) When the body was dried, materials including cassia were added. Cassia contains both linalool and cinnamaldehyde.

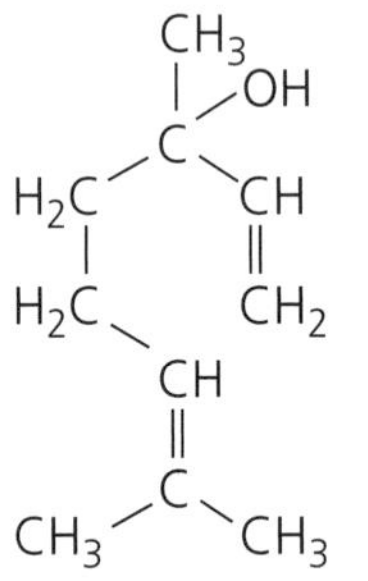

Linalool 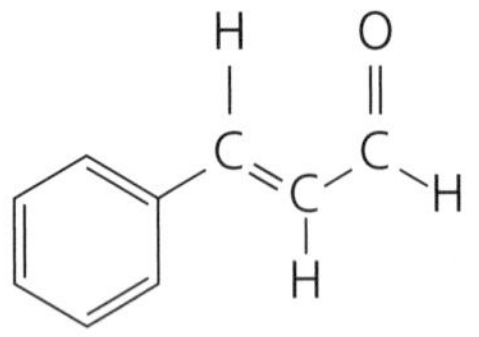   **Cinnamaldehyde**

   (i) Linalool is a terpene. Give the number of isoprene units that combine to form linalool.

          1

(ii) Explain fully why cinnamaldehyde would react with acidified potassium dichromate and linalool does not.

c) Cedar oil, which is an essential oil, is also added to the body. State what is meant by the term 'essential oil'.

9   Food scientists study the structure and properties of food molecules and the effect that the processing of food has on these molecules.

Using your knowledge of chemistry, describe the structure and properties of molecules present in food and what effects the processing of food could have on these molecules.

3

10 The nickel-containing mineral pentlandite was named after Irish scientist Joseph Pentland. A step in the process that is used to extract nickel from the mineral is shown.

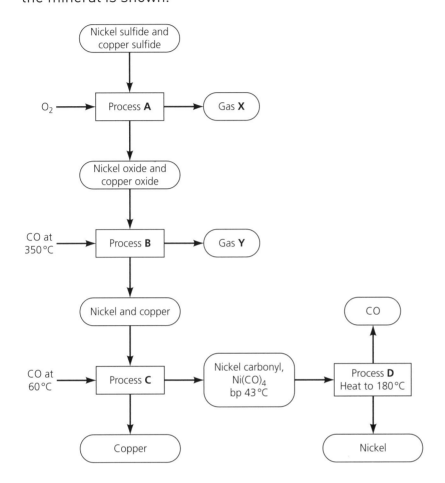

a) Suggest the names of gases X and Y.

2

b) State the type of bonding and structure of nickel carbonyl.

1

c) Draw an arrow on the diagram to show how the process could be made more economical.

1

d) Write a balanced equation for the reaction taking place in process C.

1

11 The table below shows the covalent radius and ionic radius of metal elements from period two of the periodic table.

Element	Covalent radius / pm	Ion	Ionic radius / pm
Na	154	Na^+	102
Mg	145	Mg^{2+}	72
Al	130	Al^{3+}	54
Si	117	Si^{4+}	

a) **Explain fully** why the covalent radius of the elements decreases as you move across the period from sodium to chlorine.

2

b) Ionic radius is a measure of the size of an ion.

(i) Write the equation for the first ionisation energy of sodium.

1

(ii) Predict the ionic radius of a Si^{4+} ion.

1

(iii) **Explain fully** why the ions shown are smaller than their atoms.

2

12 Chlorine molecules can split to form chlorine free radicals.

   a) Sunlight is required to split the chlorine molecules.

      (i) Name the type of radiation, present in sunlight, which provides enough energy to split the chlorine molecules.

          1

      (ii) Write the equation for this reaction.

          1

   b) State what is meant by the term 'free radical'.

          1

   c) State the name of the three stages of a free radical chain reaction.

          1

   d) Many cosmetic products contain free radical scavengers.

      (i) State what is meant by the term 'free radical scavenger'.

          1

      (ii) Name another type of product that could also contain free radical scavengers.

          1

13 A mass spectrometer is an analytical instrument that uses a beam of electrons to break bonds within molecules to form fragments. The positions of the lines in a mass spectrum correspond to the masses of the fragments that were formed.

Shown below is the simplified mass spectrum of $CH_3CH_2COCH_2CH_3$.

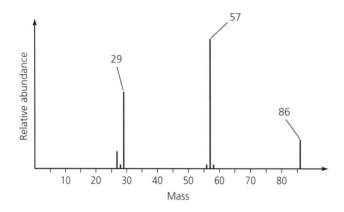

a) Give the name of the molecule used to produce the mass spectrum shown above.

1

b) The peaks at masses 29 and 57 are the result of carbon to carbon bonds being broken to form fragments.

The fragment that produces the peak at mass 57 is CH_3CH_2CO.

(i) Give the formula of the fragment that is responsible for the peak at mass 29.

1

(ii) Suggest why there is a peak at mass 86.

1

c) Another analytical technique is nuclear magnetic resonance spectroscopy or NMR for short. This process produces an NMR spectrum, which shows the number of hydrogen atoms in a molecule and their environment.

The spectrum shown below is for methylpropane.

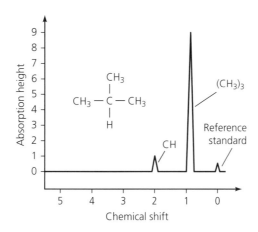

The NMR spectrum shown can be analysed using the information in the table below.

Chemical shift value	Hydrogen atom environment
0.9	—CH_3 (in an alkane)
1.3	—CH_2— (in an alkane)
2.0	—CH (in an alkane)
3.8	CH_3—O— (in an alcohol)
5.0	—O—H (in an alcohol)

(i) In the box, draw the full structural formula of the molecule which gives the NMR spectrum shown.

1

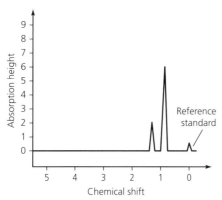

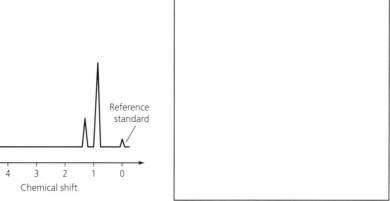

(ii) Complete the diagram below to show the NMR spectra for methanol.

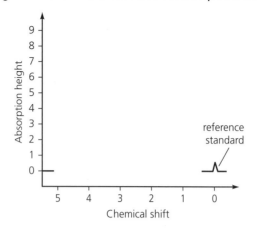

14 Yellow crazy ants spray formic acid (methanoic acid) to subdue their victims.

a) Draw the full structural formula of formic acid.

b) Formic acid can be used to produce esters such as ethyl methanoate, which can be used as a flavouring agent.

(i) Suggest another use of the ester.

(ii) Name the alcohol used to produce ethyl methanoate from formic acid.

MARKS

(iii) **Explain fully** how a sample of this ester could be produced in the lab. 2

(iv) Suggest why it would be very difficult to achieve a percentage yield of 100% for this process. 1

[END OF PRACTICE PAPER C]

C

ADDITIONAL SPACE FOR ANSWERS AND ROUGH WORK

Higher
Chemistry

Practice Paper A

Section 1

Question	Answer	Hint
1	A	The elements with the greatest difference in electronegativity will have the greatest ionic character. Refer to page 11 of the data booklet for electronegativity values.
2	B	Sodium ions (Na^+) have the electron arrangement of 2,8 and oxide ions (O^{2-}) have the electron arrangement of 2,8 so the two particles are isoelectronic.
3	C	Van der Waals forces occur between atoms or molecules. London dispersion forces, polar-to-polar attractions and hydrogen bonds are all forms of van der Waals.
4	B	The enthalpy change on the graph is the energy difference between the reactants and the products. In this case the reaction is in reverse and so the change is +20 as the reverse reaction is endothermic.
5	B	Temperature is a measure of the average kinetic energy of the particles within a substance and is measured with a thermometer.
6	D	The two functional groups highlighted are the hydroxyl (—OH) and the ester link (—COO—). It is important to learn all the functional groups and their names.
7	B	Oils are converted to fats by hydrogenation, which is the addition of hydrogen across carbon to carbon double bonds of the oil, causing it to become more saturated.
8	D	t = 1 ÷ rate and the rate at 30°C was 0.005 and therefore the time is equal to 1 ÷ 0.005 = 200 s
9	A	All fats contain the ester link functional group.
10	D	Emulsifiers prevent oil and water molecules from separating into layers by being soluble in both.
11	A	Tertiary alcohols such as option 'A' would not react with oxidising agents such as acidified potassium dichromate.
12	A	Denaturing proteins changes the shape of the molecule.
13	A	Seems tricky at first until you think that all alcohols must contain the hydroxyl functional group (—OH), which has a mass of 17 on its own so option 'A' could not possibly be an alcohol.
14	B	An alcohol, when oxidised to a ketone, loses two hydrogen atoms. Drawing out the full structural formula of 3-methylbutan-2-ol and the ketone it would form when oxidised makes this question easier to answer.
15	D	The carboxyl functional group of a fatty acid can react with the hydroxyl group to form an ester. The molecule of sucrose has eight hydroxyl groups and as a result could react with eight fatty acid molecules.
16	B	The concentration of reactants and products remains constant but not necessarily equal; this is true of all equilibrium reactions.

Question	Answer	Hint
17	**A**	Option A has only one product and so the atom economy can only be 100%.
18	**D**	A reducing agent causes another species to be reduced by supplying it with electrons and as a result the reducing agent is oxidised.
19	**C**	Three water molecules are required to balance out the three oxygen atoms. Six H^+ ions are required to balance out the six hydrogen atoms in the water; six electrons are required to balance out the charge of the six H^+ ions.
20	**B**	A pipette is used to accurately measure and transfer, from one flask to another, small volumes of liquids.

Note: References to 'HTP' indicate where relevant information can be found in Hodder Gibson's *How to Pass Higher Chemistry* book.

Question	Answer	Hint
1a)	The four hydroxyl groups and one carboxyl group contained in the glucuronic acid are polar due to the large difference in electronegativity between the hydrogen and oxygen atoms. This allows them to form hydrogen bonds with water molecules, which are also polar, resulting in the glucuronic acid being very soluble in water.	'**Explain fully**' questions require you to give lots of detail in your answer to gain the 2 marks. Including diagrams can help with your explanation. See HTP, pages 25, 29 and 30.
1b)(i)	Oxidation	Oxidation reactions convert primary or secondary alcohols into carboxylic acids. See HTP, pages 49–51.
1b)(ii)	1.0 g	**Worked answer:** *Step 1*: Work out the formula mass of potassium gluconate by adding the mass of each element together. C: $6 \times 12 = 72$; H: $9 \times 1 = 9$; O: $7 \times 16 = 112$; K: $39.1 = 232.1$ g *Step 2*: Work out the moles of potassium gluconate using moles = mass ÷ formula mass. ($5.99/232.1 = 0.026$ moles) *Step 3*: Calculate the mass of potassium using mass = moles × formula mass = 0.026×39.1 = 1.0 g. In this question you must provide the correct unit. See HTP, pages 113–115.
2	**Open question** **3 marks**: The candidate has demonstrated a good conceptual understanding of the chemistry involved. **2 marks:** The candidate has demonstrated a reasonable understanding of the chemistry involved. **1 mark**: The candidate has demonstrated a limited understanding of the chemistry involved. **0 marks**: The candidate has demonstrated no understanding of the chemistry that is relevant to the problem/situation. The candidate has made no statement(s) that is/are relevant to the problem/situation.	Open questions have no one correct answer. Listed below are **some** of the options that may be included and explained in your answer. **This list is not exhaustive and you do not have to include all of these to gain the full 3 marks**. Ensure that what you have included has been explained fully and clearly. Include diagrams, equations etc. that may help with your explanation. Collision theory Collision geometry Activation energy Kinetic energy Temperature, concentration linked to kinetic energy and collision theory Particle size linked to collision theory Catalysts Enzymes See HTP, pages 115 and 116.

Question	Answer	Hint
3a)	$CH_3OH + 1\frac{1}{2}O_2 \rightarrow CO_2 + 2H_2O$	The enthalpy of combustion is the energy released when *one mole* of a substance is completely burned in excess oxygen and as a result multiples of CH_3OH would not be accepted. $2CH_3OH + 3O_2 \rightarrow 2CO_2 + 4H_2O$ would not be awarded the mark. See HTP, page 91.
3b)	$-559.4\,kJ\,mol^{-1}$	Points to remember: $100\,cm^3$ of water is equal to 0.1 kg. All combustion reactions are exothermic and ΔH should therefore have a negative sign. **Worked answer:** *Step 1:* Calculate the enthalpy change using $\Delta H = cm\Delta T$ ($4.18 \times 0.1 \times 9.2 = -3.8456\,kJ$) *Step 2:* Calculate the moles of ethanol used using moles = mass ÷ formula ($0.22 \div 32 = 6.875 \times 10^{-3}$ moles) *Step 3:* Use this to calculate the enthalpy for 1 mole using 0.0069 moles produces $-3.85\,kJ$ then 1 mole produces ($1 \div 6.875 \times 10^{-3} \times -3.8456 = -559.36\,kJ$) See HTP, pages 91–92.
3c)	Heat lost to surroundings. Incomplete combustion. Inaccurate temperature reading due to lack of stirring. Evaporation of methanol. Impurities present in methanol	There are several reasons why the results of this experiment may be lower than expected. See HTP, page 93.
4a)		Isoprene and terpenes are asked about regularly in exams. See HTP, pages 62–63.

Question	Answer	Hint
4b)	Isoprene is in excess.	**Worked answer:** *Step 1*: Establish the molar ratio. 1 mole of isoprene reacts with 7 moles of oxygen. *Step 2*: Calculate the moles of isoprene (C_5H_8) using moles = mass ÷ formula mass (5 ÷ 68 = 0.074 moles) *Step 3*: Use the ratio to establish the moles of O_2 required, e.g. 1 mole of C_5H_8 requires 7 moles of O_2 so 0.074 moles of C_5H_8 would require 0.518 moles of O_2. (1 mark) *Step 4*: If 1 mole of oxygen is equal to 32 g then 0.518 moles is equal to 16.58 g (0.518 × 32 = 16.58 g). (1 mark) *Step 5*: Establish which reactant is in excess. As only 5 g of oxygen is available but 16.58 g is required, there is insufficient oxygen and therefore isoprene is in excess (1 mark). See HTP, pages 75–76.
4c)(i)	Terpenes	Combining isoprene molecules produces terpenes. See HTP, page 62.
4c)(ii)	Essential oils are concentrated extracts from plants, and are mixtures of organic compounds.	Do not get essential oils and essential amino acids confused. See HTP, page 62.
4d)(i)	The volatile substance is heated by using steam which has a temperature of 100°C.	This is a problem-solving question and you must read the question/diagram fully to find the answers.
4d)(ii)	219.3 g Units must be correctly stated in this answer, as they are not provided in the question. (1 mark for correct unit)	**Worked answer:** *Step 1*: 1 mole of the substance will have a volume of 24.1 litres so 0.055 litres (55 cm³) is equal to 2.28×10^{-3} moles. ((0.055 ÷ 24.1) × 1 = 2.28×10^{-3} moles) (1 mark) *Step 2*: If 2.28×10^{-3} moles has a mass of 0.5 g then 1 mole has a mass of 219.3 g. ((1 ÷ 2.28×10^{-3}) × 0.5 = 219.3 g) (1 mark) See HTP, pages 76–77.
5a)	$Na^+(g) \rightarrow Na^{2+}(g) + e^-$	State symbols must be shown for all ionisation equations. See HTP, pages 22–23.

Question	Answer	Hint
5b)	The second ionisation of an alkali metal involves removing an electron from an energy level which is closer to the nucleus and less shielded from the nucleus, therefore the nucleus has a greater influence on that electron and more energy is required to remove it. The second ionisation of a halogen involves removing an electron from the same energy level as the first electron and as a result there is not such a large increase in energy required.	**'Explain fully'** questions require lots of detail to gain the 2 marks. Including diagrams can help with your explanation. See HTP, pages 22–23.
5c)	The atomic size is increasing going down a group as the atoms have more energy levels. The screening effect of these energy levels and the fact that the outer electrons are further from the nucleus results in the nucleus having less of an influence on the bonding electrons so less energy is required to remove outer electrons.	Learn all the patterns of the periodic table and be able to explain why these changes occur. See HTP, pages 19–20.
5d)	$6895\,kJ\,mol^{-1}$ (1 mark for correct unit)	**Worked answer:** The energy required to remove the first (403), second (2633) and third (3859) must be combined. (1 mark) $403 + 2633 + 3859 = 6895\,kJ\,mol^{-1}$ See HTP, page 22.
6a)(i)	Chlorine	The chlorine atoms are reduced (gain electrons) and it is therefore the oxidising agent. See HTP, page 100.
6a)(ii)	The hydrochloric acid produced would increase eye irritation.	
6a)(iii)	484.5 kg	**Worked answer:** *Step 1*: Establish the molar ratio. 1 mole of chlorine reacts with 1 mole of hydrogen peroxide. *Step 2*: Calculate the moles of hydrogen peroxide (H_2O_2) added using moles = mass ÷ formula mass ($232\,000 ÷ 34 = 6823.5$ moles) (1 mark) *Step 3*: The 1:1 ratio shows that 6823.5 moles of H_2O_2 would react with 6823.5 moles of Cl_2 (1 mark) *Step 4*: Calculate the mass of chlorine removed using mass = moles × formula mass ($6823.5 × 71 = 484\,468.5\,g$ or 484.5 kg) (1 mark) See HTP, page 73.
6b)(i)	Free radicals have unpaired electrons and, as a result, are highly reactive.	See HTP, pages 66–67.

Question	Answer	Hint
6b)(ii)	OH• + OH• → H_2O + O_2	There was no need to balance this equation but if you did it must be balanced correctly to gain the mark e.g. OH• + OH• → H_2O + $\frac{1}{2}O_2$ or 2OH• + 2OH• → $2H_2O$ + O_2 See HTP, pages 66–67.
6c)(i)	$NCl_3(g)$ + $3H_2O(l)$ → $NH_3(aq)$ + 3HOCl(aq)	Balancing is an essential skill for any chemist.
6c)(ii)	 Potential energy (y-axis), Reaction pathway (x-axis) 	Catalysts lower the activation energy of a reaction by providing an alternative pathway. See HTP, pages 8–9.
7a)(i)	H — C — C — C — H structure with H, H, H on top and H, OH, H on bottom	The OH from the water would bond to the middle carbon atom as this has the least number of hydrogen atoms attached to it. See HTP, pages 49–51.
7a)(ii)	Propanone	Oxidation of a secondary alcohol such as propan-2-ol would produce a ketone.
7b)	Both the carbons involved in the double bond have the same number of hydrogen atoms attached.	H — C — C = C — C — H structure In but-2-ene each carbon atom has only one hydrogen atom attached and as a result Markovnikov's rule does not apply.
7c)(i)	Polarity and size of molecule	The polarity and size of a molecule affects the distance it travels up chromatography paper. See HTP, page 105.
7c)(ii)	Too much solvent has been added.	The solvent added to the beaker is above the base line and so the samples would dissolve in the solvent and not travel up the paper. See HTP, page 105.
7c)(iii)	Compound 1	See HTP, page 105.

Question	Answer	Hint
8	**Open question** **3 marks**: The candidate has demonstrated a good conceptual understanding of the chemistry involved. **2 marks**: The candidate has demonstrated a reasonable understanding of the chemistry involved. **1 mark**: The candidate has demonstrated a limited understanding of the chemistry involved. **0 marks**: The candidate has demonstrated no understanding of the chemistry that is relevant to the problem/situation. The candidate has made no statement(s) that is/are relevant to the problem/situation.	Open questions have no one correct answer. Listed below are **some** of the options that may be included and explained in your answer. **This list is not exhaustive and you do not have to include all of these to gain the full 3 marks.** Ensure that what you have included has been explained fully and clearly. Include diagrams, equations etc. that may help with your explanation. Periodic trends – covalent radius, ionisation energy, electronegativity Bonding types (intramolecular) – pure covalent, polar covalent, ionic, metallic Bonding types (van der Waal's) – hydrogen, London dispersions, permanent dipole to dipole interactions Structures – metallic, ionic lattice, covalent network, covalent molecular, monatomic Bonding continuum See HTP, pages 115–116.
9a)(i)		When drawing a structural formula, ensure that each carbon has four bonds. See HTP, pages 35–38.
9a)(ii)	Any suitable use.	Esters have many uses such as perfumes, solvents, soap manufacturing, etc. See HTP, pages 35–38.
9b)(i)	67.6%	**Worked answer:** *Step 1*: Establish the molar ratio. 1 mole of methanol reacts to produce 1 mole of methyl ethanoate. *Step 2*: Calculate the moles of methanol using moles = mass ÷ formula mass (16 ÷ 32 = 0.5 moles) *Step 3*: Use the ratio to establish the moles of methyl ethanoate produced, e.g. 1 mole of methanol produces 1 mole of methyl ethanoate so 0.5 moles of methanol would produce 0.5 moles of methyl ethanoate. (1 mark) *Step 4*: Using mass = moles × formula mass calculate the theoretical mass of methyl ethanoate produced. (0.5 × 74 g = 37 g) (1 mark) *Step 5*: Calculate the percentage yield using % yield = (actual mass ÷ theoretical mass) × 100. ((25 ÷ 37) × 100 = 67.6%) (1 mark) See HTP, pages 79–81.
9b)(ii)	The reaction is reversible.	In a reversible reaction, the product will break back down to form reactants so 100% yield is very difficult to obtain. See HTP, pages 35–38.

Question	Answer	Hint
9c)	To prevent loss of reactants and products	The wet paper towel would act as a condenser preventing the loss of the volatile reactants and products.
9d)	Esterification/condensation	It is important to learn the names of all the chemical reactions that you have covered as part of the Higher Chemistry course. See HTP, pages 35–38.
10a)		The reaction is at equilibrium when the concentration of reactants and products remains constant but not necessarily equal. See HTP, pages 85–89.
10b)	A closed system is when no reactants or products can escape.	Equilibrium can only be established in a closed system as no reactants or products escape. See HTP, pages 85–89.
10c)	The formation of but-1-ene is endothermic.	An increase in temperature favours endothermic reactions. See HTP, pages 85–89.
10d)	The chemicals are not in the gaseous state.	The chemicals are both liquids and pressure only affects the equilibrium when gases are involved. See HTP, pages 85–89.
10e)		The concentration, at equilibrium, would be the same as the previous graph. See HTP, pages 85–89.
11a)(i)	A solution of accurately known concentration.	See HTP, page 118.

Question	Answer	Hint
11a)(ii)	The standard solution is prepared by fully dissolving the correct mass of potassium permanganate in water using a beaker and transferring the contents to a standard flask. The beaker should be washed with water and the washing also transferred to the standard flask. The flask should then be made up to the meniscus with water and inverted to ensure thorough mixing.	Preparation of a standard solution is an essential skill for any chemist. See HTP, page 118.
11b)	0.44 mol l^{-1}	**Worked answer:** *Step 1*: Establish the molar ratio. 5 moles of Fe^{2+} ions react with 1 mole of MnO_4^- ions. *Step 2*: Calculate the moles of permanganate ions using N = C × V ($0.2 × 0.00875 = 1.75 × 10^{-3}$). (1 mark) The average volume of permanganate used was 8.75 cm^3. *Step 3*: Use the ratio to establish the moles of Fe^{2+} ions used ($1.75 × 10^{-3} × 5 = 8.75 × 10^{-3}$ moles of Fe^{2+}) *Step 4*: Calculate the concentration of the iron(II) sulfate solution using C = N ÷ V. ($8.75 × 10^{-3} ÷ 0.020 = 0.4375$ mol l^{-1}) (1 mark) See HTP, pages 109–110.
11c)	$MnO_4^-(aq) + 8H^+ + 5e^- \rightarrow Mn^{2+}(aq) + 4H_2O(l)$	Four water molecules are added to balance the oxygen atoms. Hydrogen ions are added to the left-hand side to balance out the hydrogen atoms. Electrons are then added to balance out the electrical charges. See HTP, pages 102–103.
11d)	22.7%	**Worked answer:** If 85 g provides 2.7 mg then 100 g provides 3.18 mg ($100 ÷ 85 × 2.7 = 3.176$) (1 mark) RDA is 14 mg so percentage of RDA is 22.7% ($3.18 ÷ 14 × 100 = 22.7\%$) (1 mark) See HTP, pages 113–115.
12a)(i)	The body cannot make all the amino acids required for body proteins and is dependent on dietary protein for supply of certain amino acids known as essential amino acids.	See HTP, pages 42–44.
12a)(ii)	During digestion, enzyme hydrolysis of dietary proteins can produce amino acids, some of which will be essential amino acids. In a hydrolysis reaction, proteins react with water, breaking down into the smaller amino acids.	During hydrolysis, the peptide link is broken and amino acids are produced. See HTP, pages 42–44.

Question	Answer	Hint
12b)	The intermolecular bonds (bonds between chains) are broken.	When proteins are heated during cooking, the intermolecular bonds are broken allowing the proteins to change shape (denature). These changes alter the texture of foods. See HTP, page 54.
12c)	Haemoglobin is polar due to the presence of the polar carboxyl functional group and can therefore form hydrogen bonding with water, which is the strongest type of van der Waals force.	The —OH section and the ═O section of the carboxyl group are both involved in hydrogen bonds with water molecules. See HTP, pages 25, 29 and 30.
12d)	6	The iron in haemoglobin has a co-ordination number of 4, indicated by the dashed lines in the diagram. The iron in hexaaquairon(II) has 6 dashed lines and as a result has a co-ordination number of 6.
12e)	–214 kJ	**Worked answer:** *Step 1*: Calculate the energy required to break the bonds in the reactant molecules. Two hydrogen peroxide molecules: $(1 \times 142 = 142)$ for the O—O bond and $(2 \times 463 = 926)$ for the two O—H bonds Total $= 1068 \times 2 = 2136$ kJ (1 mark) *Step 2*: Calculate the energy released on the formation of water and oxygen. $(2 \times 463 = -926)$ for the O—H bonds multiplied by 2 as 2 moles are produced $(-926 \times 2 = -1852)$ and $(1 \times 498 = -498)$ for the O═O bond Total $= -2350$ kJ (1 mark) *Step 3*: Combine the two to get the final answer: $2136 + (-2350) = -214$ kJ (1 mark) See HTP, page 98.

Practice Paper B

Section 1

Question	Answer	Hint
1	D	The key word in this one is 'elements'. Ionic bonds, polar covalent, and hydrogen bonds all arise as a result of differences in electronegativity and this can only occur in compounds.
2	A	The larger the difference in electronegativity the more polar a molecule will be. Electronegativity values are on page 11 of the data booklet or you can use your knowledge of periodic trends.
3	C	Activation energy is the difference in energy between the reactants and the peak of the graph. The reactants in this case are on the right as it is a reverse reaction.
4	A	Learn the periodic trends and be able to explain the patterns.
5	D	The third ionisation energy is the energy required to remove one mole of electrons from one mole of ions, in the gaseous state, with a charge of 2+.
6	A	Rate is equal to 1 ÷ time. At $1.0\,mol\,l^{-1}$ the time is 50 seconds and so the rate is $0.02\,s^{-1}$ ($1 \div 50 = 0.02\,s^{-1}$)
7	D	These questions are much easier if you draw the structural formula of each option. An isomer must have the same molecular formula but a different structure.
8	C	An aldehyde has the carbonyl functional group on an end carbon.
9	A	Soaps are produced by the alkaline hydrolysis of fats and oils to form water-soluble ionic salts called soaps.
10	D	Esters, fats and proteins are all produced by condensation reactions.
11	A	Antioxidants prevent oxidation by reducing other reactants. The iodine is reduced (gains electrons) so the $C_6H_8O_6$ is an antioxidant.
12	C	Emulsifiers are produced by the reaction of edible oils with glycerol.
13	D	This takes a bit of working out. Take each option one at a time and test to see if it works.
14	C	If 2 moles of butane require 13 moles of oxygen, then 1 mole of butane requires 6.5 moles of oxygen. If 1 mole is 24 litres then 6.5 moles is 156 litres (6.5×24).
15	B	Marketability is not an environmental consideration.
16	C	Chromatography is an analytical technique that uses difference in polarity and molecular mass to separate a mixture.
17	B	An oxidising agent causes another species to be oxidised by accepting its electrons and as a result the oxidising agent is reduced.
18	B	The enthalpy of combustion is the energy released when *1 mole* of a substance is completely burned in excess oxygen. Option B does not represent enthalpy of combustion as 2 moles of ethanol are in the equation.

Question	Answer	Hint
19	**B**	Add 6 waters to the right-hand side to balance the oxygen. Finally add *12H*⁺ to the left-hand side to balance out the hydrogen and 10 electrons to balance the charge.
20	**C**	This titration is neutralisation and would produce a salt with a pH of 7. Phenol red indicator works in the range of 6.8–8.4 and so would be suitable for this reaction.

Section 2

Note: References to 'HTP' indicate where relevant information can be found in Hodder Gibson's *How to Pass Higher Chemistry* book.

Question	Answer	Hint
1a)(i)	Distillation	Distillation can be used to separate a mixture of compounds with different boiling points. Air is a mixture of substances including noble gases such as krypton.
1a)(ii)	909 090.9 litres (1 mark for correct unit)	1 litre of krypton is 0.00011% of air so 100% is 909 090.9 $((100 \div 0.00011) \times 1 = 909\,090.9$ litres) (1 mark) See HTP, pages 113–114.
1b)	176 kJ mol^{-1}	**Worked answer:** *Step 1*: Establish the energy *required* to break the bond in the reactant molecule fluorine by referring to page 10 of the data booklet. +159 kJ mol^{-1} (1 mark) *Step 2*: Calculate the energy released when KrF_2 forms. The overall energy change for the reaction is −193 kJ mol^{-1} and if +159 kJ mol^{-1} is required to break then 352 kJ mol^{-1} must be released on formation of KrF_2 (159 + 193 = −352) (negative as it is an exothermic process). (1 mark) *Step 3*: To calculate the mean bond enthalpy the answer must be divided by two as KrF_2 has two Kr–F bonds (−352 ÷ 2 = −176). (1 mark) See HTP, page 98.
1c)(i)	$Ag \rightarrow Ag^{3+} + 3e^-$ or $2Ag \rightarrow 2Ag^{3+} + 6e^-$	Silver in this case forms a 3+ ion and this is shown by the formula AgF_3. See HTP, pages 22–23.
1c)(ii)	Krypton difluoride	An oxidising agent is reduced during a redox reaction. See HTP, page 102.

Question	Answer	Hint
2a)	Ammonia is a polar molecule because of the difference in electronegativity between the nitrogen and hydrogen atoms. This allows it to form hydrogen bonding, which is the strongest type of van der Waals attraction resulting in a relatively high boiling point. The ability to form hydrogen bonds also allows it to dissolve in water as water is also a polar molecule and therefore hydrogen bonds can form between the molecules of ammonia and water. Methane is not a polar molecule as there is very little difference in electronegativity between the carbon (2.5) and hydrogen (2.2). Methane is also symmetrical, which does not allow it to form a dipole. As a result methane can only form London dispersion forces between the molecules, which is the weakest form of van der Waals and this is shown by the low boiling point. It is also insoluble as water is a polar molecule.	This question requires lots of detailed explanation to gain all the available marks. Including diagrams in your answer can help you to gain the marks. See HTP, pages 25–32.
2b)	Sulfur dioxide is a covalent molecular substance and silicon dioxide is a covalent network.	This is not an 'explain' question and so much less detail is required. See HTP, page 26.
3a)	The four hydroxyl groups in the vitamin C molecule are polar due to the large difference in electronegativity between the hydrogen and oxygen atoms. This allows them to form hydrogen bonds with water molecules, which are also polar, resulting in vitamin C being very soluble in water.	'**Explain fully**' questions require you to give lots of detail in your answer to gain the 2 marks. Including diagrams can help with your explanation. See HTP, pages 28–30.
3b)(i)	Vitamin C is in excess.	Top tip for questions involving $N = C \times V$: Remember that the volume must be in litres. Change cm^3 into litres by dividing by 1000. *Step 1*: Establish the molar ratio. 1 mole of vitamin C reacts with 1 mole of iodine. *Step 2*: Calculate the moles of each reactant using moles = mass ÷ formula mass and $N = C \times V$ Moles of iodine = (1 ÷ 253.8 = 0.004 moles) Moles of vitamin C = (0.2 × 0.025 = 0.005 moles) (1 mark). *Step 3*: Use the ratio to establish the moles of each reactant required, e.g. 1 mole of vitamin C reacts with 1 mole of I_2 so 0.005 moles of vitamin C would react with 0.005 moles of I_2. This means that the vitamin C is in excess and therefore the iodine would have been decolourised. (1 mark) See HTP, pages 75–76.

Question	Answer	Hint
3b)(ii)	The reaction is self-indicating.	The iodine changes colour from brown to colourless so no indicator is required. See HTP, page 110.
3b)(iii)	The standard solution is prepared by fully dissolving the correct mass of vitamin C in water using a beaker and transferring the contents to a standard flask. The beaker should be washed with water and the washing also transferred to the standard flask. The flask should then be made up to the meniscus with water and inverted to ensure thorough mixing.	Preparation of a standard solution is an essential skill for any chemist. See HTP, pages 106–107.
3c)	Potassium hydroxide is an alkali and would react with the H^+ ions in a neutralisation reaction. The equilibrium would shift to the right-hand side to replace the H^+ ions removed.	This is a problem-solving question and you must read the question/diagram fully to find the answers. See HTP, pages 85–86.
4	**Open question** **3 marks**: The candidate has demonstrated a good conceptual understanding of the chemistry involved. **2 marks**: The candidate has demonstrated a reasonable understanding of the chemistry involved. **1 mark**: The candidate has demonstrated a limited understanding of the chemistry involved. **0 marks**: The candidate has demonstrated no understanding of the chemistry that is relevant to the problem/situation. The candidate has made no statement(s) that is/are relevant to the problem/situation.	Open questions have no one correct answer. Listed below are **some** of the options that may be included and explained in your answer. **This list is not exhaustive and you do not have to include all of these to gain the full 3 marks.** Ensure that what you have included has been explained fully and clearly. Include diagrams, equations etc. that may help with your explanation. Enthalpy (combustion, ionisation, bond) Activation energy Potential energy Fuels (concentrated source of energy) UV (high energy form of light) Energy requirements of industrial processes See HTP, pages 115–116.
5a)	Carboxyl and hydroxyl	It is important to learn all the functional groups. See HTP, pages 47 and 52.
5b)(i)	Two	Along with the functional groups it is also important to learn all the reactions which they take part in. See HTP, pages 53, 54, 48 and 50.
5b)(ii)	Esterification/condensation	Alcohols react with carboxylic acids to produce esters. See HTP, pages 35–36.
5c)	To prevent oil and water molecules from separating into layers.	You should also be able to explain how emulsions prevent oil and water molecules from separating. See HTP, page 60.

Question	Answer	Hint
5d)(i)	As the reactants are flammable.	Both the reactants and products in this reaction are flammable and so a Bunsen burner should not be used.
5d)(ii)	To prevent boiling off the ethanol.	Ethanol has a boiling point of 78°C and if the temperature exceeded this then it would be evaporated.
5d)(iii)	60.45 g	**Worked answer:** *Step 1*: Establish the molar ratio. 1 mole of ethanol reacts to produce 1 mole of ester. *Step 2*: Calculate the moles of ethanol using moles = mass ÷ formula mass (23 ÷ 46 = 0.5 moles). *Step 3*: Use the ratio to establish the moles of ester produced, e.g. 1 mole of ethanol produces 1 mole of ester so 0.5 moles of ethanol would produce 0.5 moles of ester. (1 mark) *Step 4*: Using mass = moles × formula mass calculate the theoretical mass of ester produced (0.5 × 186 g = 93 g) (1 mark). *Step 5*: Calculate the mass by multiplying the theoretical mass of ester by 65% (93 × 65% = 60.45 g). (1 mark) See HTP, pages 79–81.
6	**Open question** **3 marks**: The candidate has demonstrated a good conceptual understanding of the chemistry involved. **2 marks**: The candidate has demonstrated a reasonable understanding of the chemistry involved. **1 mark**: The candidate has demonstrated a limited understanding of the chemistry involved. **0 marks**: The candidate has demonstrated no understanding of the chemistry that is relevant to the problem/situation. The candidate has made no statement(s) that is/are relevant to the problem/situation.	Open questions have no one correct answer. Listed below are **some** of the options that may be included and explained in your answer. **This list is not exhaustive and you do not have to include all of these to gain the full 3 marks.** Ensure that what you have included has been explained fully and clearly. Include diagrams, equations, etc. that may help with your explanation. Esters Terpenes UV radiation Sun block Free radicals – formation, structure and chain reactions Free radical scavengers Fragrances Essential oils Soaps See HTP, pages 115–116.
7a)(i)	2,2,4-trimethylpentane	

Question	Answer	Hint
7a)(ii)	22.9°C	**Worked answer:** Top tips for questions involving $\Delta H = cm\Delta T$ Remember that 500 cm³ of water is 0.5 kg. Remember that all combustion reactions are exothermic and ΔH should therefore have a negative charge. *Step 1*: Calculate the moles of hydrocarbon used using moles = mass ÷ formula $(1 \div 114 = 8.77 \times 10^{-3}$ moles) (1 mark) *Step 2*: Combustion of 1 mole of the hydrocarbon releases -5460 kJ mol^{-1} so 8.77×10^{-3} moles will release 47.89 kJ ($8.77 \times 10^{-3} \times 5460 = 47.89$ kJ). (1 mark) *Step 3*: Use the energy released to calculate the temperature change using $\Delta T = \Delta H \div cm$ $(47.89 \div (4.18 \times 0.5) = 22.9°C)$. (1 mark) See HTP, pages 91–92.
7a)(iii)	Pure oxygen is used. Complete combustion. No heat lost to surroundings.	Any of the reasons listed will gain you the mark. See HTP, page 93.
7b)(i)	C_6H_6	A straightforward one!
7b)(ii)	Bromine test. The bromine would be decolourised if carbon to carbon double bonds were present (addition reaction).	Bromine is used to test for unsaturation i.e. the presence of a carbon to carbon double bond.
7b)(iii)	$+46$ kJ mol^{-1}	**Worked answer:** Top tip for Hess's Law questions 1. Remember to balance the equations. 2. Remember to reverse the enthalpy sign when reversing an equation. 3. Remember to multiply the enthalpy value when multiplying an equation. You will need the balanced equations for the combustion of carbon and hydrogen. Equation 1: $C(g) + O_2(g) \rightarrow CO_2(g)$; $\Delta H = -394$ kJ mol^{-1} Equation 2: $H_2(g) + \frac{1}{2}O_2(g) \rightarrow H_2O(g)$; $\Delta H = -286$ kJ mol^{-1} Equation 3: $C_6H_6(l) + 7\frac{1}{2}O_2(g) \rightarrow 6CO_2(g) + 3H_2O(l)$; $\Delta H = -3268$ kJ mol^{-1} (1 mark) To match the target equation, equation 1 must be multiplied by 6, equation 2 has to be multiplied by 3 and equation 3 must be reversed. (1 mark) The enthalpy values can then be combined $((6 \times -394) + (3 \times -286) + 3268 = +46)$. (1 mark). See HTP, pages 93–97.

Question	Answer	Hint
7c)(i)	$2H_2(g) + O_2(g) \rightarrow 2H_2O(l)$	The 'H_2' equation must be multiplied by 2 so that there are equal amounts of electrons in both equations. Both the H^+ ions and electrons are cancelled out. See HTP, page 100.
7c)(ii)	Water is the only product.	The cell does not produce CO_2 or other pollutant gases.
8a)	The covalent radius is increasing going down a group as the atoms have more energy levels. The screening effect of these energy levels and the fact that the outer electrons are further from the nucleus results in the covalent radius increasing.	'**Explain fully**' questions require you to give lots of detail in your answer to gain the 2 marks. Include diagrams in your answer if you think it will help with your explanation. See HTP, pages 19–20.
8b)	The larger the covalent radius the lower the first ionisation energy.	
8c)	$Cs^+ (g) \rightarrow Cs^{2+} (g) + e^-$	The second ionisation energy is the energy required to remove the second electron from an ion in the gaseous state. See HTP, page 22.
8d)	All Group 1 metals have one outer electron. The first ionisation energy is the energy required to remove the electron from the outer energy level. The second ionisation requires an electron from an energy level closer to the nucleus and which is less shielded by inner energy levels to be removed and as a result more energy is required.	'**Explain fully**' questions require you to give lots of detail in your answer to gain the 2 marks. Include diagrams in your answer if you think it will help with your explanation. See HTP, page 22.
8e)(i)	Electronegativity is a measure of the attraction an atom involved in a bond has for the electrons of the bond.	'State' questions should be straight recall. See HTP, pages 20–21.
8e)(ii)	The covalent radius is increasing going down a group as the atoms have more energy levels. The screening effect of these energy levels and the fact that the outer electrons are further from the nucleus results in the nucleus having less of an influence on the bonded electrons and therefore a lower electronegativity.	'**Explain fully**' questions require you to give lots of detail in your answer to gain the 2 marks. See HTP, pages 19–20.
9a)	Alkaline hydrolysis	This reaction forms water-soluble ionic salts called soaps. See HTP, pages 58–59.

Question	Answer	Hint
9b)	During cleaning using soaps the hydrophobic tails dissolve in a droplet of oil or grease, whilst the hydrophilic heads face out into the surrounding water. Agitation of the mixture results in ball-like structures forming with the hydrophobic tails on the inside and the negative hydrophilic heads on the outside. Repulsion between these negative charges results in an emulsion being formed and the dirt released.	The terms hydrophobic and hydrophilic are important terms to be aware of and describe in terms of soap molecules. See HTP, pages 58–59.
9c)	Detergents do not form a 'scum' in hard water areas.	See HTP, pages 59–60.
10a)	To remove/absorb water	A tricky one that requires some thought.
10b)	0.52 g	**Worked answer:** Step 1: Establish the molar ratio. 1 mole of carbon dioxide is produced from 1 mole of malachite. Step 2: Calculate the moles of CO_2. 1 mole = 24 litres then 56 cm³ equals 2.3×10^{-3} moles $(0.056 \div 24 = 2.3 \times 10^{-3})$ (1 mark) Step 3: Use the ratio to establish the moles of malachite used e.g. 1 mole of CO_2 requires 1 mole of malachite so 2.3×10^{-3} moles of CO_2 would require 2.3×10^{-3} moles of malachite. (1 mark) Step 4: Calculate the mass of malachite using mass = moles × formula mass. $(2.3 \times 10^{-3} \times 221 = 0.52 \,g)$ See HTP, pages 76–77.
10c)(i)	Carbon monoxide	Carbon monoxide is a commonly used reducing agent in industry. See HTP, page 100.
10c)(ii)	59.1%	**Worked answer:** Step 1: Calculate the formula mass of CuO (79.5) and add to the formula mass of CO (28). Step 2: Calculate the % atom economy using % atom economy = mass of desired product ÷ mass of reactants ×100 $(63.5 \div (79.5 + 28) \times 100 = 59.1\%)$ See HTP, pages 81–82.
10c)(iii)	The kinetic energy of the particles must be greater than the activation energy and the collision geometry must be correct.	Collision theory can be used to explain the effects of concentration, pressure, surface area, temperature and collision geometry on reaction rates. See HTP, pages 4–7.

Question	Answer	Hint
11a)	Peptide link or Amide link	Proteins contain the peptide link. $$\begin{array}{cc} O & H \\ \parallel & \mid \\ -C- & N- \end{array}$$ See HTP, pages 42–44.
11b)(i)	Hydrolysis	In a hydrolysis reaction a molecule reacts with water, breaking down into smaller molecules, in this case amino acids. See HTP, pages 42–44.
11b)(ii)		The peptide link can be seen here. When drawing a full structural formula make sure that all bonds are included and are attached to the correct atom of the functional group. See HTP, pages 42–44.
11b)(iii)	The body cannot make all the amino acids required for body proteins and is dependent on dietary protein for supply of certain amino acids known as essential amino acids.	See HTP, pages 42–44.
11c)	When proteins are heated during cooking, intermolecular bonds are broken allowing the proteins to change shape (denature). This change alters the texture of foods.	This change in structure has a large impact on the protein. You can see this happening when an egg is cooked. As the protein in the egg white is denatured a visible colour change occurs. See HTP, page 54.
11d)(i)		Markers assess these questions by asking 'Would this work as drawn?' All labels should be included and the measurements on the measuring cylinder/syringe must be shown. Ensure that the delivery tube does not have a line drawn across it at any point as this is classed as a blockage. See HTP, page 118.
11d)(ii)	33.3 s	T = 1/rate. The rate at 30°C is $0.03\,s^{-1}$. Time = 1 ÷ 0.03 = 33.3 seconds See HTP, page 10.

Question	Answer	Hint
12a)		The carbonyl group of a ketone is not on an end carbon. Ensure that all bonds and hydrogen atoms are correctly drawn. See HTP, pages 49–51.
12b)	Any of the following: Acidified dichromate solution Tollens' reagent Fehling's reagent	Aldehydes can be oxidised to form carboxylic acids but ketones cannot. Using one of the oxidising agents listed would produce a positive result with aldehydes but no reaction with a ketone. See HTP, page 51.
12c)	Primary alcohol	Primary alcohols can be oxidised to form aldehydes, secondary alcohols are oxidised to form ketones and tertiary alcohols cannot be readily oxidised. See HTP, pages 49–51.

Practice Paper C

Section 1

Question	Answer	Hint
1	B	Argon has the electron arrangement of 2,8,8 but it is not a negatively charged particle. Chlorine will gain an electron to form a negatively charged particle with the electron arrangement of 2,8,8.
2	C	The first ionisation energy is the energy required to remove 1 mole of electrons from 1 mole of atoms in the gaseous state.
3	D	The mass would decrease as the reaction proceeds as a gas is given off. All the other measurements would produce an increasing measurement as the reaction proceeded.
4	B	Pure covalent bonds (no difference in electronegativity between atoms) and ionic bonds (caused by a large difference in electronegativity) are at opposite ends of the bonding continuum.
5	C	Fluorine is the most electronegative element in the periodic table.
6	A	Isoprene has the systematic name of 2-methylbuta-1,3-diene.
7	C	Hydrogenation is the addition of hydrogen across the carbon to carbon double bond to change an unsaturated compound into one which is saturated.
8	A	You should also be able to draw the structural formula of glycerol (propane-1,2,3-triol).
9	D	2-methylbutan-2-ol is a tertiary alcohol and as a result would not react with an oxidising agent. Drawing out the full structural formula of each option can make answering questions like this easier.
10	D	All enzymes contain the peptide link and are therefore classed as proteins.
11	B	It is important to learn the colour changes associated with the oxidising agents Tollens' reagent, acidified potassium dichromate, acidified potassium permanganate and Fehling's reagent.
12	A	The addition of a catalyst has no effect on the position of equilibrium but does allow equilibrium to be established more quickly.
13	D	Remember to balance the chlorine before adding water and H^+ ions. The ClO_3^- molecule must be multiplied by two to balance the chlorine. $$2ClO_3^- + 12H^+ + 10e^- \rightarrow Cl_2 + 6H_2O$$
14	C	Changes in pressure do not affect reactions with no gases involved or with an equal number of moles of gas on each side of the equation.
15	D	The resulting gas mixture would be composed of $30\,cm^3$ of unreacted oxygen gas and $10\,cm^3$ of carbon dioxide.
16	C	The combination of reaction W → X (−50), X → Y (−86) and Y → Z (−74) gives the overall energy change for the reaction. Note that the equation for Z → Y must be reversed.
17	B	The enthalpy change is the difference in energy between the reactants and products.

Question	Answer	Hint
18	**A**	This is a tricky one and requires you to refer to page 12 of your data booklet. Only dichromate ions ($Cr_2O_7^{2-}$) are below bromine in the electrochemical series and as a result would oxidise bromide ions.
19	**A**	Redox reactions involve both oxidation and reduction reactions taking place. In option A, the magnesium atoms are oxidised and the hydrogen ions are reduced.
20	**A**	The average used should be the average of concordant results only and so only titres 2 and 4 should be used, as titres 1 and 3 are not concordant.

Section 2

Note: References to 'HTP' indicate where relevant information can be found in Hodder Gibson's *How to Pass Higher Chemistry* book.

Question	Answer	Hint
1a)	Covalent molecular	Both covalent and molecular must be stated as the question asks for the bonding and structure.
		The state symbol given in the equation for stannic chloride ($SnCl_4$) is liquid and this suggests that it has a low melting point and therefore is more likely to be a covalent molecular substance.
		See HTP, page 26.
1b)	$Sn^{2+} \rightarrow Sn^{4+} + 2e^-$	The tin(II) ions are converted to tin(IV) ions by losing two electrons.
		See HTP, page 100.
1c)	56.5%	**Worked answer:**
		Step 1: Calculate the formula mass of $HgCl_2$ (271.6) and add to the formula mass of $SnCl_2$ (189.7).
		Step 2: Calculate the % atom economy using % atom economy = mass of desired product ÷ mass of reactants × 100 (260.7 ÷ (271.6 + 189.7) × 100 = 56.5%).
		See HTP, pages 81–82.
1d)	Any correct description of the following: Decant (pouring off the top layer to leave the bottam layer behind). Separating funnel. Use of a dropper to remove the top layer.	Mercury has a density of 13.5 g cm^{-3} (page 5 of the data booklet) and so the stannic chloride would form as a layer on top of the mercury.
1e)(i)	Self-indicating reaction	The potassium permanganate changes colour as the permanganate ion is converted to a manganese ion. The colour change is purple to colourless.
		See HTP, page 110.
1e)(ii)	26.9 cm^3	The results of titrations 2 and 4 should be used, as they are concordant results.
		See HTP, page 119.

Question	Answer	Hint
1e)(iii)	0.01 moles	**Worked answer:**
		Top tip for questions involving $N = C \times V$
		Remember that the volume must be in litres. Change cm^3 into litres by dividing by 1000.
		Step 1: Establish the molar ratio, 5 moles of oxalic acid reacts with 2 moles of permanganate.
		Step 2: Calculate the moles of permanganate using $N = C \times V$.
		Moles permanganate = (0.04 × 0.0269 $= 1.076 \times 10^{-3}$ moles) (1 mark)
		Step 3: Use the molar ratio to establish the moles of oxalic acid contained in the $25\,cm^3$ portion $((1.076 \times 10^{-3} \div 2) \times 5 = 2.69 \times 10^{-3}$ moles) (1 mark).
		Step 4: Multiply the number of moles by four as the question asks for moles 'contained in $100\,cm^3$' and the experiment only used $25\,cm^3$ (1 mark)
		$(2.69 \times 10^{-3} \times 4 = 0.01$ moles) (1 mark).
		See HTP, pages 109–110.
1f)	2884.6 g	If 100 g of leaves contains 0.52 g of oxalic acid, then to obtain 15 g of oxalic acid you would require 2884.6 g of leaves. $((15 \div 0.52) \times 100 = 2884.6\,g)$
		See HTP, pages 113–114.
2a)	The hydroxyl groups of both molecules are polar due to the large difference in electronegativity between the hydrogen and oxygen atoms. This allows them to form hydrogen bonds with water molecules, which are also polar, resulting in both molecules being soluble in water.	'**Explain fully**' questions require you to give lots of detail in your answer to gain the 2 marks. Including diagrams can help with your explanation.
		See HTP, pages 25–30.
2b)	Hydroxyl and amide (peptide) link	It is important to learn the names of all the functional groups and how to identify them.
		See HTP, pages 42 and 47.
2c)	The peptide link (amide link) of the molecule may hydrolyse in the presence of water.	See HTP, page 43.

Question	Answer	Hint
3	**Open question** **3 marks**: The candidate has demonstrated a good conceptual understanding of the chemistry involved. **2 marks**: The candidate has demonstrated a reasonable understanding of the chemistry involved. **1 mark**: The candidate has demonstrated a limited understanding of the chemistry involved. **0 marks**: The candidate has demonstrated no understanding of the chemistry that is relevant to the problem/situation. The candidate has made no statement(s) that is/are relevant to the problem/situation.	Open questions have no one correct answer. Listed below are **some** of the options that may be included and explained in your answer. **This list is not exhaustive and you do not have to include all of these to gain the full 3 marks**. Ensure that what you have included has been explained fully and clearly. Include diagrams, equations etc. that may help with your explanation. Chromatography Volumetric analysis – titrations (acid/base and redox) Oxidation – oxidising agents (Fehling's (Benedict's), Tollens', acidified dichromate solution) Flame tests Testing properties – solubility, melting point, pH, etc. See HTP, pages 115–116.
4a)	Increasing the temperature increases the kinetic energy of the particles. This means that more reactant molecules have a kinetic energy greater than the activation energy, resulting in more successful collisions and so a faster reaction.	'Explain fully' questions require you to give lots of detail in your answer to gain the 2 marks. Including diagrams such as the one shown below can help with your explanation. See HTP, pages 4–6.
4b)(i)		This gas cannot be collected over water because it is very soluble in water. See HTP, pages 118 and 119.

Question	Answer	Hint
4b)(ii)	0.12 g	**Worked answer:** *Step 1*: Establish the molar ratio. 1 mole of copper reacts to produce 1 mole of sulfur dioxide. *Step 2*: Calculate the moles of sulfur dioxide using the molar volume $((0.045 \div 24) \times 1 = 1.875 \times 10^{-3}$ moles) (1 mark). *Step 3*: Use the ratio to establish the moles of copper produced, e.g. 1 mole of Cu produces 1 mole of SO_2 so 1.875×10^{-3} moles of SO_2 would require 1.875×10^{-3} moles of Cu. (1 mark) *Step 4*: Using mass = moles × formula mass calculate the mass of copper reacted $(1.875 \times 10^{-3} \times 63.5\,g = 0.12\,g)$. (1 mark) See HTP, page 74.
5a)	Equal and usually different	At equilibrium the concentration of the reactants and products remains constant, but not necessarily equal. See HTP, page 85.
5b)	$$K = \frac{[H^+]^2[SO_3^{2-}]}{[SO_2][H_2O]}$$	Pay attention to the balancing of the equation as $2H^+$ results in $[H^+]^2$ shown in the equation.
5c)	Strong acids break up completely into ions and the H^+ of the acid would react with the OH^- of the alkali in a neutralisation reaction. The same reaction would occur with the weak acid and even though it only dissociates partially the removal of the H^+ ions due to the neutralisation reaction would result in the equilibrium shifting to the right-hand side and causing the weak acid to fully dissociate.	This is a tricky one and requires you to demonstrate a good knowledge of equilibrium. Including equations in your answer will help with your explanation. See HTP, pages 85–86.
6a)	Glycerol/propane-1,2,3-triol	See HTP, page 38.
6b)	Oleic acid is unsaturated meaning that it contains carbon to carbon double bonds. These bonds cause the oil molecule to have a distorted structure making it more difficult for them to pack closely together, resulting in fewer van der Waals attractions between the oil molecules. It therefore requires less energy to melt the molecule than a fat as they can form lots of van der Waals attractions as they can pack closely together.	'**Explain fully**' questions require you to give lots of detail in your answer to gain the 2 marks. Including diagrams can help with your explanation. See HTP, pages 38–39.
6c)	Hydrogenation	The addition of hydrogen across the double carbon to carbon bond turning unsaturated oils into a saturated fat is called hydrogenation. See HTP, pages 38–39.

Question	Answer	Hint
6d)(i)	A titration could be performed with the iodine. The iodine would add across the double bonds in an addition reaction resulting in the iodine becoming colourless. When a brown colour remains then the iodine is in excess. The more iodine added to the fatty acid before the brown colour remains, the greater the degree of unsaturation.	When describing procedures such as this titration always include a description of expected results. See HTP, pages 117 and 119.
6d)(ii)	Oils are not soluble in polar molecules such as water but are soluble in non-polar solvents such as hexane.	See HTP, page 30.
7a)	Carbonyl functional group	Learn all the names of the functional groups and how to identify them. See HTP, page 50.
7b)	Correct description of oxidation with an oxidising agent and correct colour change with butanal only.	Ketones such as butanone cannot be oxidised but aldehydes such as butanal can be oxidised to form carboxylic acids. See HTP, pages 49–52.
7c)	$-276\,kJ\,mol^{-1}$	**Worked answer:** Top tip for Hess's Law questions 1. Remember to balance the equations. 2. Remember to reverse the enthalpy sign when reversing an equation. 3. Remember to multiply the enthalpy value when multiplying an equation. You will need the balanced equations for the combustion of carbon and hydrogen. **Equation 1** $C(g) + O_2(g) \rightarrow CO_2(g)$; $\Delta H = -394\,kJ\,mol^{-1}$ **Equation 2** $H_2(g) + \frac{1}{2}O_2(g) \rightarrow H_2O(g)$; $\Delta H = -286\,kJ\,mol^{-1}$ **Equation 3** $C_4H_8O(l) + 5\frac{1}{2}O_2(g) \rightarrow 4CO_2(g) + 4H_2O(l)$; $\Delta H = -2444\,kJ\,mol^{-1}$ To match the target equation, equation 1 must be multiplied by 4, equation 2 must be multiplied by 4 and equation 3 must be reversed. (1 mark) The enthalpy values can then be combined $((4 \times -394) + (4 \times -286) + 2444 = -276)$. (1 mark) See HTP, pages 93–97.
8a)(i)	(Alkaline) Hydrolysis	See HTP, page 58.
8a)(ii)	During cleaning using soaps the hydrophobic tails dissolve in a droplet of oil or grease, whilst the hydrophilic heads face out into the surrounding water. Agitation of the mixture results in ball-like structures forming with the hydrophobic tails on the inside and the negative hydrophilic heads on the outside. Repulsion between these negative charges results in an emulsion being formed and the dirt released.	The terms hydrophobic and hydrophilic are important terms to be aware of and describe in terms of soap molecules. See HTP, page 59.

Question	Answer	Hint
8b)(i)	Two	Isoprene (2-methylbuta-1,3-diene) has five carbon atoms per molecule and the terpene linalool has 10 carbon atoms. See HTP, pages 62–63.
8b)(ii)	Cinnamaldehyde is an aldehyde, contains the carbonyl group on an end carbon, and as such can be oxidised to form a carboxylic acid. Acidified potassium dichromate is an oxidising agent and would oxidise the aldehyde. Linalod is a tertiary alcohol and cannot be oxidised.	'Explain fully' questions require you to give lots of detail in your answer to gain the 2 marks. See HTP, pages 51–52.
8c)	Essential oils are extracted from plants. They have distinctive smells and contain terpenes.	See HTP, pages 62–63.
9	**Open question** **3 marks**: The candidate has demonstrated a good conceptual understanding of the chemistry involved. **2 marks**: The candidate has demonstrated a reasonable understanding of the chemistry involved. **1 mark**: The candidate has demonstrated a limited understanding of the chemistry involved. **0 marks**: The candidate has demonstrated no understanding of the chemistry that is relevant to the problem/situation. The candidate has made no statement(s) that is/are relevant to the problem/situation.	Open questions have no one correct answer. Listed below are **some** of the options that may be included and explained in your answer. **This list is not exhaustive and you do not have to include all of these to gain the full 3 marks**. Ensure that what you have included has been explained fully and clearly. Include diagrams, equations, etc., that may help with your explanation. Esters Carboxylic acids Aldehydes and ketones Fats and oils Oxidation Hydrolysis Addition (hydrogenation) Emulsions Proteins See HTP, pages 115–116.
10a)	X – Sulfur dioxide Y – Carbon dioxide	See HTP, page 71.
10b)	Covalent molecular	The low boiling point of 43°C suggests that the bonding and structure must be covalent molecular. See HTP, pages 14 and 26.

Question	Answer	Hint
10c)		Industrial processes recycle as much as possible to reduce costs. See HTP, pages 70–71.
10d)	$4CO + Ni \rightarrow Ni(CO)_4$	
11a)	Going across the period the atomic charge increases. This means that the outer electrons are more tightly held which pulls the outer energy level closer to the nucleus.	Learn all the patterns of the periodic table and be able to explain why these changes occur. See HTP, pages 19–20.
11b)(i)	$Na(g) \rightarrow Na^+(g) + e^-$	The first ionisation energy is the energy required to remove 1 mole of electrons from 1 mole of atoms in the gaseous state. The state symbols must be shown in the equation. See HTP, page 22.
11b)(ii)	$42 \rightarrow 46$	A tricky one that requires some thought.
11b)(iii)	When metals form ions they lose their outer electrons to achieve a stable electron arrangement like a noble gas. When they lose their outer electrons they have one less outer energy level resulting in a smaller radius.	Learn all the patterns of the periodic table and be able to explain why these changes occur. Including diagrams in your answer can help with your explanation. See HTP, page 22.
12a)(i)	UV or ultraviolet radiation.	See HTP, page 66.
12a)(ii)	$Cl_2 \rightarrow Cl\bullet + Cl\bullet$	The chlorine molecule would split to form single chlorine atoms called free radicals. See HTP, page 67.
12b)	Free radicals have unpaired electrons.	It is the unpaired electrons which make free radicals very reactive. See HTP, page 66.
12c)	Initiation, termination and propagation	You must be able to recognise initiation, propagation and termination steps of a free radical chain reaction and be able to write equations for these steps given relevant information. See HTP, page 67.

Question	Answer	Hint
12d)(i)	Free radical scavengers are molecules that can react with free radicals to form stable molecules and prevent chain reactions.	See HTP, page 67.
12d)(ii)	Food or plastics	They are added to food to prevent the food from going off too quickly. See HTP, page 67.
13a)	Pentan-3-one	Use the shortened formula to get the name. The position of the carbonyl group must be identified as there are two possible positions within the molecule. See HTP, page 50.
13b)(i)	CH_3CH_2	The molecule fragments and the fragment shown has a mass of 29.
13b)(ii)	Not all of the molecules have fragmented.	The original molecule of pentan-3-one has a mass of 86 so the peak shown at this mass must be the result of unfragmented pentan-3-one.
13c)(i)		The peak at 0.9 is due to the CH_3 group and the peak at 1.3 is due to the CH_2 group.
13c)(ii)		Peaks must be shown at 5.0 (— O—H bond) and 3.8 (CH_3—O—).
14a)		
14b)(i)	Perfume, solvent, etc.	Esters have many uses. See HTP, page 37.
14b)(ii)	Ethanol	Esters are produced by a reaction between an alcohol and a carboxylic acid. The ethyl part of the ester name comes from the parent alcohol ethanol. See HTP, page 35–36.

Question	Answer	Hint
14b)(iii)	Small quantities of ethanol and methanoic acid are mixed in a test tube. Concentrated sulfuric acid catalyst added. Wet paper towel condenser at mouth of test tube. Cotton wool plug at top of test tube. Test tube placed in a water bath (no naked flames). After some time, the test tube is added to a beaker of sodium hydrogen carbonate solution. (To neutralise the acid catalyst) Layer of ester should form on top of the solution.	'Explain fully' questions require you to give lots of detail in your answer to gain the 2 marks. A description similar to this would gain the marks. Include diagrams to help with your description. See HTP, pages 35–36.
14b)(iv)	Reversible reaction	The reaction is reversible so there will always be some of the product that breaks back down to produce an alcohol and a carboxylic acid.